The Art of Relaxation

The Art of
Relaxation

HERMAN S. SCHWARTZ

Illustrated by Thomas Carron

New York
THOMAS Y. CROWELL COMPANY

Manufactured in the United States of America
by the Vail-Ballou Press, Inc., Binghamton, New York.

Library of Congress Catalog Card No. 54-5612

Dedicated to the memory of
H. J. GREY
whose inspirational encouragement
and benevolent aid made this
volume possible.

Introduction

A SOLID generation of dedicated study about people in trouble is represented in this compact work by Herman S. Schwartz. In these pages appear the concentrated fruit of a lifetime of interest in individuals undergoing some kind of stress experience. Whenever a veteran participant-observer of the human scene makes available to the public the essence of his knowledge, the reader may be assured that he "knows whereof he speaks."

The author is here concerned to "do something" for the unknown public clients who have been motivated to turn to these pages to learn the Art of Relaxation. They must receive positive assistance in dealing with the uncomfortable manifestations of a restless spirit. Such aid must be immediate, concrete, and practical in nature or it is little more than a hoax played on the numerous victims of the tension produced by current modes of living. It must also meet the test of constant availability plus simplicity and ease of application.

This "Schwartz approach" appeals to all who need to have at their command a fairly comprehensive system of responses for lessening the recurring common strains of our time. Quite properly, the average man insists on understanding and controlling the relatively trivial situations in which he is the central figure as well as more imposing phenomena. There is some reason for believing that our inner peace is more often menaced by lack of mastery over comparatively petty stimuli than by the objective menace to mental ease of threats on a grander scale.

A popular diffusion of the most useful insights of modern psychology has already done much to lessen the strains and improve the quality of our educational and economic activities; but there is a limitless area for betterment in the relatively untouched realm of purely domestic and private satisfactions. In this broad field the author of the present volume is very much at home. He speaks with the clear voice of a level-headed and unpretentious student of relaxation. Those who listen critically to his message should remember that there is a technology of little things as well as of big.

No student of the intricacies of personality is so naïve or immodest as to claim that every variety of behavioral difficulty will disappear with one application of his favorite remedy. However, it is both sound lay wisdom and good laboratory science to hold that if tension in the organism is a prominent symptom of some underlying trouble then whatever conduces to a relaxed state will further the search for an adequate solution. The material presented in this volume may confidently be employed as contributing to that important aim.

George W. Hartmann, Chairman
Department of Psychology
Roosevelt College of Chicago

Acknowledgments

It is with a deep sense of appreciation that acknowledgment is made to those who have extended fully to the author their willing co-operation with the various problems that presented themselves in creating this work.

The author had the good fortune of obtaining the editorial collaboration of Professor George W. Hartmann, Chairman of the Psychology Department of Roosevelt College; Glenn Long, Editor of *Healthways Magazine;* and Miss Page Cooper, author and editor.

I also wish to express my gratitude to Benjamin Daublin; Arthur Liebers, author and editor; and Dr. C. W. Weiant for their careful readings and pertinent advice. Special thanks are extended to my capable secretary, Miss Amy Paul, who patiently and skillfully performed the laborious task with the entire manuscript. I am also indebted to my wife and son, whose affection and understanding made my task easier.

And finally, I acknowledge my debt of gratitude to Mr. William Poole, Editor in Chief of the Thomas Y. Crowell Company, whose encouragement and guidance was a source of deep inspiration.

The author has freely consulted the books listed on pages 200–205, to verify his independent findings and own approach to the subject of relaxation.

Contents

1.

Relaxation
and the Life Rhythm

MENTALLY WORN OUT?
HOW ARE YOUR CONTROLS?
THE BODY'S RHYTHMOSTAT

> . . . If you should individually achieve calm-
> ness and harmony in your own person, you may
> depend upon it that a wave of imitation will
> spread from you as surely as the circles spread
> outward when a stone is dropped into a lake.
> —WILLIAM JAMES

IN THESE tense and anxious times, relaxation is the key
to physical ease, mental peace, and spiritual tranquillity.
Unless we master the basic life rhythm, we are headed for
some kind of physical or mental trouble. But you, no doubt,
have already recognized this. And it was your personal need
for relaxation which led you to this book.

Through these pages *you can learn ways to peace of body
and mind without any professional aid whatsoever.* You
can learn to maintain or regain normal composure, assurance, and fitness—and with no "rest cure" except short
periods in an easy chair, at your desk, or reclining on a bed
or cot. This workable plan has evolved from thirty years

1

of study and experience. It is based on simplified and practical ideas of modern psychology and physiology. It will produce both mental and physical relaxation in a remarkably short time.

Furthermore, this is a method which *you* can *teach yourself*. In the independent democratic tradition of depending on yourself, you can learn to conserve and revitalize the resources of both your body and your mind. You will find it a stimulating and useful adventure.

You will learn exactly what type of relaxation *you* need for the work *you* do, whether you are a housewife, an executive, a salesman, clerk, student, mechanic, lawyer, merchant, or chief. Because everyone—sick or well, weak or strong, active or inactive—needs to relax. *Whether you are fidgety or well-composed, high-strung or lethargic, happy or gloomy, busy or retired, you need to rid yourself of your imbedded nerve tensions.*

But first we should define what we mean by "relaxation."

The word is often applied to a pleasant or diverting recreational activity. We like to think of ourselves as "relaxing" when we indulge in a physical sport or when we watch prominent athletes performing for our benefit. Any form of entertainment, such as going to a play, a movie, a night club, or watching TV, is said to be relaxing. So too are social conversation, parlor games, the pursuit of hobbies, and even the much maligned daily setting-up exercises. In fact, any change from our usual business activities is commonly considered beneficial to our nervous system.

But such "recreational relaxation," though desirable, requires physical or mental energy. These particular forms of relaxation will be discussed in due course, but they are not our chief concern in this book.

"Relaxation" as defined here is the rest segment in life's action-inaction cycles, inseparable from the rhythmic laws of nature. It is a "breathing spell"; a recuperative rest; temporary relief from fatigue, from tenseness of nerves and muscles, from worries, anxieties, resentments, frustrations, pains and aches, and related disturbances. It is a restorative pause from excess activity by planned and habitual periods of rest for body and mind.

To be relaxed means being at ease with your work, your duties or obligations, your aspirations, your victories, and your defeats. It means facing each day unafraid, being the confident master of your problems rather than their apprehensive or cringing slave.

Yet let us not expect relaxation to offer us a total escape from everyday problems. We need a certain amount of the nerve-muscle tension that these problems generate. Without the *stress* of living, we become mentally soft and physically helpless, and as inadequate as the loose strings of a violin played upon with the loose hairs of its bow. So *it is the control of tension that we must master. A knowledge of relaxation is the key to the successful use of tension.*

Having determined what we mean by relaxation, let us consider your greatest present need. Do you need more relaxation in your home? On your job? Are you tense while driving? Do you or your children have difficulty in studying? Do you become tense with your hobbies? Do your emotions get the best of you? Do you fear loss of your health? Is ambition driving you frantic? Do you get yourself upset in your attempt to go to sleep? Within this book, you will find ways to cope with those common life situations.

And now—because one purpose of this book is to help you *immediately*—let us digress for a moment in the interest of the relaxation you may need, *right this minute*.

If you have just had a trying day, or are expecting one tomorrow, skip the rest of this chapter now and look in the Index for the information touching upon your immediate problem. You may be conscious at this moment of some strain—of the eyes, the neck and shoulders, the feet, the low-back region, or the like. By following the suggested exercises, you may be able to gain a measure of ease.

But let us warn you not to *pursue* relaxation. *Submit* to it. If the electric light by which you are reading is too harsh, reduce it to a softer glow. Sit without strain in your favorite chair. If music is available, and you enjoy it, let it be soft and soothing, like a summer zephyr that gives a sense of well-being without intruding upon the consciousness.

Then after you have found how to relieve your immediate problem, come back to these introductory thoughts tonight, or tomorrow—whenever you can, to gain better self-understanding and better insight as to your attitudes toward yourself and others.

But it is only fair to admit that this is by no means a "cure-all" book. It is *not guaranteed* to make you healthy, wealthy, or generally wise! Nevertheless proper rest periods, even of short duration, will noticeably increase your efficiency. And the time taken to recuperate will repay you tenfold in renewed energy and vigor.

In addition, you can learn to recognize nervous tension not only in yourself but in others as well. This is an invaluable asset in getting along with people. You will learn that your relaxation may have a chain reaction that will calm the other person. And this book will teach you how to supply such a touch of relaxation when it is needed.

MENTALLY WORN OUT?

We must learn how to slow down in order to give ourselves a chance to recuperate from strenuous efforts, to insure ourselves continued clarity of vision, steadiness of disposition, and vigor of body.

Driven as we are by love, hate, fear, ambition, or by any other set of violent emotions, we *seem* to adjust ourselves to almost all difficulties, even to the dangerous point of near-exhaustion, when all reserve energy is dissipated. *We work too hard and expect too much of ourselves—and of others.* These and other contributory factors cause us to get used to chronic tiredness until slowly, accumulated weakness creeps up, and we cannot carry on any longer. We may be unaware of our mounting tenseness or irritability until conditions are so far advanced that we have become mentally worn out. The overanxious individual is like a person walking in the dark toward a precipice.

This, in a nutshell, is part of the story behind most of the "nervous breakdowns" which, according to the National Institute of Mental Health, occur to nine million persons annually, and these figures take no account of the many others who are hovering on the edge of emotional collapse. Mental illness strikes one member of every fifth family in the United States; 55 per cent of the available hospital beds are occupied by mental patients. No one is immune to nervous exhaustion in its astonishingly varied forms. But the nervous or overburdened person can continue to function effectively in all his manifold spheres of activity if he is systematic about *taking definite periods of complete, deliberate, and controlled rest.*

The basic rules presented here are designed to give you this controlled rest. If you follow them, your rest or sleep in any comfortable position will be much more peaceful. When you arise, your mind and body will be refreshed and your thinking definitely clearer. Moreover, the probabilities are overwhelming that you will be able to obtain greater comfort and peace of mind and body than you have experienced since babyhood. We offer this not for the sake of a pleasant regression to infancy, but as a means for better health, and the ultimate attainment of whatever goals you have set for yourself.

HOW ARE YOUR CONTROLS?

The natural inborn controls of your body need conscious assistance. We must never lose sight of the fact that we are designed to conform to the universal laws of rhythm, change, and stability.

We were born with natural sensitivity to all the laws that operate to maintain the one universal scheme. To the extent that we understand and comply with these laws, we obtain peace of body and mind. In the degree that the natural laws are opposed and violated, we create disharmony. Normally, these laws operate automatically through the body's "built-in" controls. By learning how to make use of these controls, you will not only acquire ways to cope with immediate troubles, but by forming proper habits you can build for yourself a system of instinctive behavior that will benefit your entire future.

It is vital that we know at least a little about the marvels of these built-in control mechanisms. As highly civilized beings, we suffer from divers ailments that seemingly do not afflict primitive peoples and lower animals. This is not because our mechanical construction is inferior. It is caused by our failure to keep pace with the demands made upon us physically and mentally by our highly geared civilization.

A few supremely blessed individuals seem to possess instinctively the knowledge of how to maintain stability of body and mind. A few others are blessed with seemingly indestructible bodies. Such persons do not need the counsel of this book. It is to those who must make a conscious effort to achieve health and tranquillity that these pages are dedicated.

THE BODY'S RHYTHMOSTAT

Let us remember that natural controls within us do exist and that they perform the all-important services of maintaining our well-being. Most familiar to us, perhaps, is the thermostatic or temperature control of our bodies. Whether we are at the "North Pole" or the Equator, our body's temperature is normally within a fraction of 98.6 degrees.

And then we have the automatic control system of the heart. It governs the normal adult rhythm of seventy-two beats per minute and maintains balance in the performance of the heart and circulatory system. If it is not abused, it increases or slows the beat automatically, according to the demands upon it. But this cardiostatic mechanism can be impaired by excess work, worry, injury, disease, neglect, and abuse.

The appetite mechanism also functions automatically. The sight of a luscious melon or the aroma of a broiling steak causes the mouth to water and digestive fluids to flow. In the realm of romance, a young woman places her fingertips on the arm of her lover and the heart leaps, the blood races. Let these stimuli run riot into gourmandising and lust, and the control mechanisms involved will be carrying dangerous overloads.

Our brain also responds to our emotions, thoughts, and actions. Man's worst emotions may overpower his best thoughts to the extent that he is impelled to actions that are immoderate and patently injurious. All this adds up to an overload on the automatic controls—the built-in regulators—of the nervous system, the system which maintains the normal tone of tissue and poise of mind that mark the ideal, self-possessed, competent person "always at his best."

Now let us consider the master control mechanism of the body—the nervous system. From or through it all the other systems get their cues. The nervous system contains a natural action-inaction rhythmic regulator of living that we have called the "rhythmostat." Practically speaking, the attainment of peace of body and mind depends upon our awareness of and obedience to this "built-in" regulator that governs all of our internal machinery, and that should also govern our behavior.

To see the rhythmostat working at its best, observe the so-called "dumb" animals. They know when to play and run, when to stop and rest. And when they rest, they rest profoundly and completely. Watch any pet dog and you will be convinced. In fact all God's creatures but harassed and hurried civilized man—including you, my friend—obey implicitly the rhythm of living. Yet we must obey it or we hinder our future growth and expose ourselves to disease.

As a result of ignoring our natural rhythmostat, our nerves, muscles, and emotions become overstrained through excessive or prolonged activity; or we grow lethargic and weak through inactivity. Just as continued extreme heat or cold will break down the automatic operating of the body's thermostat, so will continued nerve-muscle tension or excessive ease break down the body's rhythmic control. This governing instrument must be set right again by a revised program of sound-living habits.

We seldom need to drive ourselves. There is no necessity to go without rest until a task is finished. Great minds in all ages have learned that their efficiency and creativeness were in no way diminished by their obedience to the body's need for rest. Relaxed living can be obtained—or regained —if we attune our inner ear once more to the essential nature of our being. *We need zestful work and play, frequently broken by complete mental-physical repose.*

Life itself is a perfect rhythmic duo of activity and rest. We see it throughout Nature. Humanity is subject to the same laws! Normally, you react instinctively to this action-inaction cycle. Once you understand how to keep in tune with the rhythm of the universal forces operating in and through the body, and practice relaxation regularly, your individual life will be enriched.

As mature individuals, it is not only necessary to obey the organic rhythm on a purely physical basis. We must extend this control of our physical system to our ethical areas of living, such as respect for self and others and a spirit of give and take, live and let live. For it is in these areas that most of us go wrong and need a complete re-education at periodic intervals in our adult lives.

2.

Why Relax?

DANGERS OF TENSION · PHYSICAL CONTROL
CAUSES OF TENSION
HOW TO RECOGNIZE YOUR NERVOUS TENSION
WARNING SIGNALS OF OVERSTRAIN

DANGERS OF TENSION

WE ARE living under a diversity of outside stresses; yet we are compelled to control most of our instinctive drives "from within." This continual struggle between external natural and social forces and our instinctive drives is likely to result in illness of one form or another whenever a weakness within our organism develops.

The muscle or nerve tautness that is caused by these stresses may be so deep that we are unaware of it. Indeed, it may be so elusive that sensitive electrical measuring devices are required to detect it. Yet it can keep us in a constant state of irritability. It's as though we wound up a watch and then unwittingly every few minutes "kept on winding it up." If we are not aware of what is happening, we naturally make no effort to "unwind" ourselves.

Do you need proof that this may apply to you personally?

Watch people deep in thought. Note especially their muscular action between and around the eyes. Observe their
facial expressions when they are worried, fearful, perplexed, exasperated, angry, or tired. They stiffen the body,
knit the brow, wring the hands, helping to "tighten themselves up in a knot."

Facial tension unfortunately can become habitual. The
tenseness gradually envelops the neck, the scalp, and finally
extends to the back of the skull. The tightness or rigidity
continues until it envelops the entire muscular body. When
we are angry, notice how tense our hands become and how
our movements are quickened. Recall how numb and semi-
paralyzed we become when fear suddenly seizes us. Watch
the perplexed or nervous individual, as he paces up and
down the room, or slumps in a chair in a contorted position;
the way he sits with legs crossed, arms folded across the
chest, neck twisted, meanwhile continually puffing at a
cigarette, chewing gum, or talking excitedly.

Our body is made of flesh and bone, as well as spirit, all
interconnected with the integrated and unifying brain and
nervous system. The nervous system, structurally an elonga-
tion of the brain itself, extends from the base of the skull,
through the vertebral canal, and the openings of the verte-
brae of the backbone, finally penetrating every gland, organ, muscle, bone, and tissue, ending in the cells in remot-
est and deepest parts of our body, as well as our fingertips,
toes, and skin. Therefore, when *any* muscles are tense, there
is inevitably a reaction, in greater or lesser degree, upon
the *entire* nervous system. The greater the amount of *local*
tension, the greater the *general* nervous irritability.

Everything we do, everything we experience, everything
that happens inside our body, and everything that can happen to us from outside our body affects our nerve system
in either a beneficial or a detrimental way. If our nervous

system lacked this power of response, we would be all but nonexistent. But when these stimuli are hurtful, or become unbearable in intensity, pain or distress will follow. If such stimuli, or irritants, did not produce pain, the body, or the particular part of it that is primarily affected, would deteriorate, finally becoming diseased and useless.

PHYSICAL CONTROL—THE GATEWAY TO EMOTIONAL CONTROL

. You will notice that, when tension sets in, the affected part of the body winces or constricts in its attempt to escape the distressing stimuli. This occurs when we have a headache, a stiff neck, or any other pain. Often *these tensions remain* to plague us long after the original irritant is gone. As you know, these leftover tensions can result from many causes. Whatever its source, it is likely to produce a corresponding mental attitude of depression or irritability.

And just as physical tensions can produce a blue mood, so control of our muscles may chase it away. Since the nervous system is continually affecting the rest of the organism, the way we walk or talk influences the way we feel and think. If we look and behave as if we were happy, we have gone a long way toward making our make-believe come true.

So it is important to understand and practice body control. A first lesson is to learn to tolerate minor annoyances. Hold the thought in your mind, "I can take it," "It will soon pass." For instance, when a man in the barber chair is being shaved with a sharp razor, he avoids the temptation to make quick movements of his head or body to eliminate a slight pain or itch, and, surprisingly enough, the irritation subsides.

Similarly, when one has an impulse to cough, the impulse

can be controlled by inhaling a slow, deep breath and exhaling slowly and resistantly. This refers only to the dry, hard, "unproductive" cough. When it is loose, there is no need to hold it back for it clears the bronchial tubes.

As we see that minor irritations can either be taken in their stride or controlled, we realize the value of relaxation. It is not a cure, a true cure must go much deeper, but it gives us a stopgap interval of rest during which the recuperative forces of our body can do some mending.

These periods in which our minds are at ease give us also an opportunity to discover why we permit ourselves to become so irritated. Listed below are the more usual reasons.

CAUSES OF TENSION

1. Fatigue, caused by lack of sleep or excess activity or inactivity.

2. Being "musclebound." The large muscles built up through youthful participation in active sports are, in maturity, commonly allowed to become rusty, unused machines, calling for action.

3. Eating or drinking too much, or a diet deficient in the basic nutritive elements, the proteins, mineral salts, or vitamins.

4. Dehydration or being waterlogged.

5. Retention beyond a safe or comfortable interval of accumulated body wastes.

6. Poor blood circulation that allows fatigue toxins to be retained in your body.

7. Hidden minor neurological irritations.

8. Lack of understanding about your nature, and about how to control your emotions.

9. Faulty basic attitudes toward yourself and toward the problems with which you have to cope.

10. All sorts of disturbing social, political, and economic pressures.

11. Adverse environmental influences, such as noises, odors, bad lighting, excess heat or cold.

12. Holding aroused emotions in check while your body manufactures *excess* glandular fluids, such as adrenalin, thyroxine, sexual hormones, or other biochemicals. These circulate in the blood system as accumulated physical energy, and usually find no satisfactory outlet. Such inhibited emotional drives when stifled, continue nonetheless to over-stimulate the brain and nervous system. Thus, though civilization imposes desirable moral regulations, your nerves pay the price of such harmful inhibitions. Primitive man, at a moment's challenge, released the tensions created by glandular stimulation in "fight or flight." He did not sit placidly while emotions seethed within him.

13. Excess relaxation, better known as sheer laziness. Lack of interest in the job, indifference to the needs of others—or just plain boredom with living.

14. The "tension of success" can also make the middle-aged person feel buoyant with a boundless sustained false energy that can affect such organs as the arteries, heart, or stomach. The spirit may be as young as ever; but you must recognize the toll that age and time take of the physical mechanism. There can be danger to your health in the sensation of "never felt better in my life," if it stems from the pressure of excessively stimulated living.

These and other complex biological disturbances or adverse situations may irritate the brain, nerves, or muscles, singly or in combination. As a result you may become fatigued, depressed, hateful, fearful, excited, and confused; in short, in anything but in buoyant health.

HOW TO RECOGNIZE YOUR NERVOUS TENSION

The first warning of *your* need for a method of relaxation to establish normal physical and mental tone is your awareness of the persistent tenseness within you. Briefly, let us touch upon the most common indications of accumulated tensions in order that you may recognize their nature and something of the problems with which you must cope.

Casually check your score on the following tests:

1. Do you "fly off the handle" at the least provocation, and later regret your explosive behavior? Hang-over tension, stemming from some hidden recesses of your mind or body, causes you to lose your temper.

2. When you rest, do you get up fully refreshed in body and mind, perfectly at ease, ready to start work again? Or do you go back to your regular work with an effort—with the same muddled confusion in your thoughts, and aching weariness in your body? If so, you do *not* completely relax while you are resting. Although you may have seemed to be in repose, in reality, neither your muscles nor your mind were at *ease*.

3. When someone else is temporarily taking over your duties or place in the home or at work, are you *completely off the job?* Or do you continue to worry about what goes on during your absence?

4. Lift up the empty sleeve of your coat as it hangs on a nearby chair. When you let go of it, it drops by itself. Now test the muscle tension of your arm by trying this on yourself. Lift up your right arm at the wrist with the assistance of your left hand. Then let go of it. It should drop into your lap as quickly and heavily as did the sleeve of your coat.

But when you are tense, this usually occurs: instead of permitting the left hand to lift up the right arm, your right arm will instinctively raise itself. (Trying this several times will prove that it is so.) When you let the arm go, it either remains in midair by itself or falls into your lap slowly and hesitatingly.

Try test 4, and it will very likely prove to you that you are tense. When your arm and shoulder are relaxed, they should approximate the limpness and looseness of the sleeve of your hanging coat. You will then have an idea of the state in which your entire body should be when it is fully relaxed.

When completely relaxed, the arm will drop heavily of its own accord, like the action of the arm of a rag doll or a sleeping child. You will neither help raise it, hold it in midair, nor drop it lightly. So why not stop reading now and try this simple test?

5. When sitting with your eyes closed, do your eyes

twitch, and your fingers move? Do you shift in your chair, constantly seeking a more comfortable position? Do you easily become startled at minor noises, and annoyed at the slightest irritations? Is it an effort to avoid doing these things, or do you feel yourself becoming rigid when you try to control yourself?

6. Are your important face muscles tense? Are your teeth clenched as you read this, or is there some space between them for the tip of your tongue? Smile, and see if there is any appreciable difference in the space between your teeth.

It is sometimes difficult to examine ourselves and detect the symptoms of nervous strain in our behavior but the following warning signals are easily recognizable:

WARNING SIGNALS OF OVERSTRAIN

1. Do usual noises begin to sound louder; for example, does the tick of any clock become annoying?

2. Do lights to which you have been accustomed start to appear much brighter or dimmer or in any way irritating?

3. Are ordinary annoyances, such as a dripping faucet, unbearable?

4. Does a picture which has been hanging slightly off center for days or weeks without evoking comment, suddenly become a source of irritation?

5. Does it become an effort for you to talk, or does your own voice sound unusually hoarse or loud?

6. Do comparatively easy or familiar tasks become difficult or unpleasant?

7. Do you have a sustained loss of appetite (not attributable to some disease process)?

8. Are you repeatedly unable to fall asleep at your usual retiring hour?

Of course, if *all* the above symptoms are present, simple relaxation is not enough. Extreme tenseness may indicate a need for proper nourishment, a change of feeling or attitude, better self-understanding, correction of mechanical nerve interferences, or the removal of adverse environmental factors. In that case you will want to consult your doctor. He will probably recommend relaxation in addition to his treatments.

If you are unable to pass these simple tests to your own satisfaction, you should be convinced that you are under some kind of residual tension. These and other nervous reactions are clearly noticeable in the person who is fidgety, or looks irritated. They are even more dangerous to the health of those individuals in whom they are *not noticeable*. Those superficially placid or poker-faced people seem to be well-poised and under perfect control; they always *look* calm, cool, and collected. But the *retained or "bottled-up"* stress ultimately reacts on their arteries, organs, joints, nerves, or glands, and plays even more havoc than it does on those who occasionally "blow off steam" or fidget it off.

Do not be discouraged if you are not able to relax immediately. Perhaps you are not getting results for one of the following reasons.

1. You may be too critical or too analytical, expecting too much from your first attempt at relaxation.

2. Perhaps your nerve irritations are so deep within you that relaxation is insufficient to make any inroads upon the tensions that they produce.

3. It may be necessary for you to take some vigorous exercise to throw off some of the excess mental excitability before your body can relax.

4. Possibly an important matter is uppermost in your mind, and you will either have to attend to it or make a memo before your muscles will quiet down.

3.

Preparatory to Physical Relaxation

CHAINED TO A SCHEDULE

THE world of scheduled precision into which we were born—a world filled with clocks, calendars, timetables, programs, and date books—also increases our nervous tension. We were fed by measured formulas at definite times, and all our habits were precisely formed by the hands of a watch, virtually from the hour of our birth.

In childhood, most of us had to be in school at an exact time. We had to learn the same things in the same way. Our learning was graded by precision percentages, and all our school sports and exercises were precisely given. (Only recently have some schools made real provisions for individual differences among pupils.)

Now, as adults, we literally get up with "alarm," we eat in haste, and we rush to catch the 8:15 so we can punch the precision clock. Whether we teach school, are telephone operators, or run a machine, our work must typically be exact and precise all day long. At the precise moment after work, we rush to the dense traffic of subway, bus, or car, which is stopped by time-set lights, and started again by synchronized switches.

We arrive home for a meal cooked by precision recipes and served with corresponding exactitude. After dinner, we rush to catch the precision programs of the movie, radio, or television. We expect the children to obey in clocklike behavior. The precision father looks upon the most obvious demand of a child as a nuisance; and *the precision mother never creates a real home*.

Even our funeral services are arranged on exact schedules. We must make our last exits promptly, because another corpse is timed to follow us in twenty minutes. Thus we continue to race ourselves all through life, and with exactitude, rush ourselves to our graves.

Many of us are so trained in precision that even a refreshing pause is looked upon as a monkey wrench in our unhappy merry-go-round, and arouses a sense of guilt. The slaves of exactitude bring unhappiness to themselves and others. The most unfortunate aspect of all this is that when we become too rigid or fixed in our thinking and in our behavior, our tenseness contributes heavily to the incipient nervous breakdown. At our peril, we lose sight of the fact that rest is as important a part of life as action. Is it any wonder that our nerve tenseness becomes deeply embedded within us whether or not we are aware of it?

A conscious practicing of relaxation is the best way of counteracting the strains engendered by our schedule-driven lives. The following suggestions will help reduce the tensions, and properly prepare you for relaxation.

Surroundings.

First of all, in your home, reserve a room, or a corner of a room, as your place for relaxation. Establish it in your mind as a cherished spot of ease and serenity, at the threshold of which you shed your current cares. Let no burdens and worries intrude there. Let it be quiet, with mellow lighting, with a comfortable, firm bed, or cot, and perhaps an easy chair.

AIR.

Good circulation of air in the room is essential. Should the air however be too cold, or should there be a draft, complete relaxation can be hindered. Do not seek to receive the maximum amount of outdoor fresh air when attempting to get the fullest relaxation.

COLOR.

Soft or pastel shades of blue, green, and gray are normally conducive to relaxation. Such quieting colors play a useful preliminary role.

MUSIC.

To overcome some initial difficulty in relaxing mind or body, certain types of music can be helpful. For this purpose, none but personally agreeable instrumental compositions are indicated. While it is true that any sound is inherently distracting, yet if the *outer* musical "noise" succeeds in drowning out the *inner* mental noises, then music is good, even if perfect ease does not immediately result.

EASING MINOR BODY ACHES AND PAINS

Remove as much physical discomfort as possible, so that you will be able to relax completely. Do not overlook any health factors conducive to your personal ease. If your distress is mild, you will find some relief by the use of simple age-old remedies which are always at hand. The use of a cold sponge or cloth on the forehead helps remove superficial congestion from the skull. If your nostrils are congested, clear them; a minute of nasal massage may make breathing easier. Yawning also may help. If your throat is sore, massage the sides of your neck as though you were washing; do it with downward strokes. The application of a cold, wet napkin under a small dry towel will also give a measure of relief. Mild heat applications to the feet have a soothing effect.

Remove all irritants that act as barriers to relaxation. At all points of the body, free yourself from tight or confining clothing whenever possible. Remove shoes, have stockings pulled away from the toes. Loosen collars, bras, garters, corsets, belts, etc.

POSITION OF THE BODY

Lie flat on your bed or on a cot. (If any part of your body is uncomfortable, support it by a small, soft pillow. Some people, however, may find these extra pillows a distraction to true relaxation.) There is no particular advantage in resting on your back unless you find it most conducive to your comfort. The human body is just as heavy whether we are resting on the back, side, or front of it. If you are accustomed to resting in baby fashion on your chest and abdomen, there is no reason why you cannot stretch and relax in that position, using two extra pillows, one placed under your chest and one under your abdomen. Also place a small pillow under your shinbone near the instep. Then the main part of your body is comfortable on these supports, and your neck and head are comparatively free in performing the simple exercises.

POSITION OF THE HEAD

When lying on the back *the perfect placing of the head is a prime necessity*, as it removes much of the strain from the muscles of the neck, head, scalp, and forehead. Here is how: In the pillow, punch a dent for the rounded bump at the back of the skull. The hump of the pillow should then act as a support for the hollow back of the neck. The head

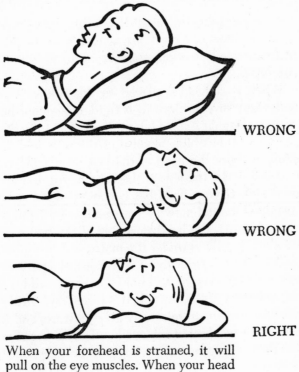

WRONG

WRONG

RIGHT

When your forehead is strained, it will pull on the eye muscles. When your head is resting freely and comfortably, as shown in the correct position, you re- move all possible pull. Thus, it is easier for your eye muscles to become relaxed.

should assume exactly the same easy or correct position in relation to the body while lying down as when sitting or standing. The head is then neither pressed forward nor backward (see illustration).

Assume this new position while lying down. To satisfy yourself as to the ease it produces, perform these two tests:

1. Lie without the head pillow for about two minutes.
2. Elevate your head very high for several minutes.

After observing the relative discomfort produced by these two uncomfortable positions, again adjust the pillow in the recommended position, and notice the restored ease and comfort.

When your head is placed on the pillow, if your scalp feels tight, or your neck feels rigid, move your head about or massage your scalp a bit, until you feel fully at ease. The person who has high blood pressure may find it advantageous to raise the head of the bed by placing two blocks of wood under the legs at the head board, imitating a hospital bed. If your head has become congested because of sustained mental activity (especially of a fretful or worrisome nature), the headward part of the bed can be lifted by placing pillows *under* the mattress.

The reason for the above is obvious. If a person sleeps on too many pillows, he will not be at ease, and his back may sag; whereas, if the entire bed is raised and tilted, his body contour remains in relatively good posture, and the elevation of the head is not achieved at the expense of an uncomfortable feeling in the neck region or between the shoulders.

If your head is congested for any reason, you may be unable to rest until you have walked for a while to remove the stagnant venous blood from your brain. These blood vessels may become swollen, from excess study or emotion, as your feet and legs may become perceptibly swollen from excessive walking. Moderate exercise in the open air increases the amount of oxygen in the brain, which in turn reduces the lactic acids and other brain-cell fatigue toxins.

This exercise creates a certain measure of relief, because it re-establishes the necessary *equilibrium of circulation*. It is conducive to relaxation.

Whether or not you do anything more preparatory to relaxation, the foregoing arrangements will add immeasurably to your well-being, and they are the perfect setting for the work of our next and master chapter.

4.

The Essence of Bodily Relaxation

INDIVIDUALIZED RELAXATION
THE MUSCLE STRETCH · TESTS BEFORE RELAXATION
THE PROGRAM · EXERCISES
THE FINAL TOUCH · IS RELAXATION EFFORTLESS?
AVOID "MUSTS" · DON'T GO TO SLEEP!
HOW LONG SHALL I REST?
DANGERS OF PROLONGED RELAXATION
TESTS FOR RELAXATION CAPACITY
ABBREVIATED FORM OF RELAXATION

INDIVIDUALIZED RELAXATION

RELAXATION, in its most simplified and natural form, need not be performed with precise conformity to any inflexible system. The formulas presented in this chapter should not be regarded as rigid rules. Feel free to change them to suit your convenience, reactions, body contour, and resting habits. The basic aim is: *Get yourself into complete mental and physical repose, and remain that way for a given time.*

No one can tell you explicitly how much you should exercise. The amount of exertion you expend, or the amount of rest taken between relaxation exercises, varies considerably depending upon such factors as your physique, age, your general health, muscle tone, and the time you have been accustomed to spending in exercising.

Although it is not essential, it will be helpful if someone reads to you, while you follow these directions. Then reverse the procedure—you read and let the other person follow through the instructions. By working together, errors you might make in procedure will become obvious to both you and your partner, and you'll consequently learn more swiftly.

But you can learn the art of relaxation by yourself if you adhere to the instructions that follow.

You have probably been under sustained tension ever since you were a child. Hence, you cannot hope to achieve the ultimate in relaxation at the first few tries. Do not become impatient. And do not try too hard to make headway at once, for overeagerness will defeat your chief purpose—the achievement of soothing relaxation.

Learning a new skill requires application. First, *grasp the main idea;* then slowly add other pertinent details. Finally, with practice, you will become skillful. Some time must necessarily elapse before proficiency is attained.

We have reduced this entire method to its most elementary components, so that you will be using the least strenuous means to acquire relaxation. Remember, do not start with the intention of making it a job, a chore, or a duty. Emphatically, the important thing is to become more and more at ease.

THE MUSCLE STRETCH

To attempt to obtain physical relaxation while your muscles are kinked or taut is an error made by laymen as well as authorities. Better and quicker results are possible through the *double-stretching exercises* described below.

Your muscles work in groups. You activate only one set of muscles when you stretch your leg down. You activate another group (its antagonists) when you resistantly pull your leg back to position. Thus it is advisable, for purposes of vitalizing as well as freeing your muscles from strain or tension, to perform the double muscular stretch. This is a slow-motion double muscular stretch from beginning to end; safe, efficient, and timesaving. But we beg you to remember that this muscular act must be performed deliberately, slowly, and rhythmically.

The form of stretching advocated here is based upon observations of how a child or animal stretches instinctively. If an animal or child unconsciously knows enough to perform this primary beneficial muscular act, surely the adult by conscious and intelligent effort should be able to duplicate this instinctive movement.

A safe rule is: *Start all stretching exercises, including yawning, by holding your abdomen under control,* bring your abdominal muscles *in toward your back and up toward your shoulders.* When there is an effort to keep them under control, then stop stretching. If your breathing is labored, if your heart races, or your face becomes flushed, it means that you have worked too hard at it.

A word of caution is necessary. Take it easy! Do not stretch any part of your body quickly or to the fullest extent. In your eagerness, you might sprain a muscle or tear a ligament. Even trained athletes occasionally "pull" a muscle, and the chances are that you are far from being in the pink of condition. Only when your muscles become strengthened should you increase this effort. If you are not sure how far to go, give yourself the benefit of the doubt by doing less. As long as you are careful, you will be unlikely to strain yourself.

Perform all the exercises that follow while lying in bed or on a wide couch. The entire relaxation procedure should take about a half hour. With some practice, you should be able to do it in less time. For the balance of your allotted time, remain in absolute repose.

Set a time to relax when nothing need interfere with your regime. If you determine to relax, let us say from one o'clock to one thirty, then during that time, you are simply "not at home" to telephone calls, ringing doorbells, or distractions of any kind. You immobilize your mind and body; you achieve tranquillity; you decide ahead of time that during this period, you are going to be completely at peace.

You are now in a quiet room, and have set your alarm or given instructions not to be disturbed for the next half hour. You are ready to come to the very heart of the relaxation process. It is simplicity itself.

TESTS BEFORE RELAXATION

Before you start your exercises, perhaps you would like to make written notes of how you feel, to be checked later for benefits derived. Note:

1. The present condition of your body as far as the stiffness of your muscles is concerned.

2. Your slight bodily irritations, if any.

3. Your present reactions to possible noises within your hearing.

4. The present intensity of your worries, anger, fretfulness, etc.

5. What mood you are in at this time. Do you feel depressed, excited, discouraged, etc.?

6. Close your eyes for a moment. Then note how they feel—if they are heavy, tired, sleepy, or strained.

THE PROGRAM

STRETCH. Slowly stretch one part of your body at a time, while all your other muscles are *relatively* at ease. Establish rhythm in these stretching exercises. You can master it more easily by timing the stretch to the count of five. When you have established rhythm, you may discontinue the count.

PULL BACK (RESISTANT RELEASE). Do not permit your muscles to become quickly released from the stretch. They should not snap rapidly into another condition. Offer resistance (hold back). Pull the muscles back to normal in the same length of time as it took to stretch them. The sensation experienced throughout should be as though someone were restraining you from allowing your muscles to become at ease. Through the pull back of your muscles a slight stretching occurs in other adjacent and remote muscles that you ordinarily would not exercise.

MUSCLE WRIGGLE. After the stretched part of your body has come to rest, wriggle, shake, or move that limb or part into a completely comfortable position. This is necessary to eliminate the possible slight strain produced through the stretching, as well as to decrease your imbedded muscular tension. It will also increase your blood circulation.

REST PERIOD. Allow the exercised muscles and your entire body to remain completely at rest for about two minutes or more (as long as you feel tired from the exercise).

During this rest period, ease the exercised muscles by holding the thought of "quiet." Your mental alertness is important. Note how the part of your body which you exercised feels in comparison with the part which you have not yet exercised. Or recall how tense your muscles were before and note how relaxed they are now; how good it is to get yourself purposefully into a state of repose; how easy these exercises are.

Luxuriate. Get the feeling, the taste of relaxation

as you get the taste for food so that at the mere thought your mouth waters and digestive juices start to flow. When this has happened in connection with these exercises, you will have only to direct your thought of relaxation to any part of your body and relaxation will start.

If you do not take the rest periods between exercises, you miss a vital part of this procedure. You may fail to experience the release from tension and the clear feeling of muscular well-being that should follow the exercises.

But if, instead of being in a contented frame of mind, you become restless or agitated, take a brisk walk, make some notes about your problem, or take a warm bath. Then later, again try relaxation.

EXERCISES

Follow all general rules given above. Do the stretching exercises in three distinct parts. First is the usual firm stretch; second, you pull your muscles back so that you will activate the other muscles which you usually neglect to stretch. Finally, you wriggle yourself out of all possible remaining strain. This will help your body to become completely limp and at ease. Do not move again during the self-assigned two-minute period of rest.

1. Lie on your back. To the slow count of five, stretch downward the *lower right side of your body*. Don't raise your leg off the bed. You should feel a slight stretch throughout the small of the back, hip, and entire leg, down to the spread-out toes (shoes having been removed). SPEND THE SAME AMOUNT OF TIME IN S-L-O-W-L-Y PULLING BACK ALL THE MUSCLES TO NORMAL. REPEAT THIS SEVERAL TIMES. THEN SPEND ABOUT A HALF-MINUTE IN WRIGGLING THEM INTO COM-

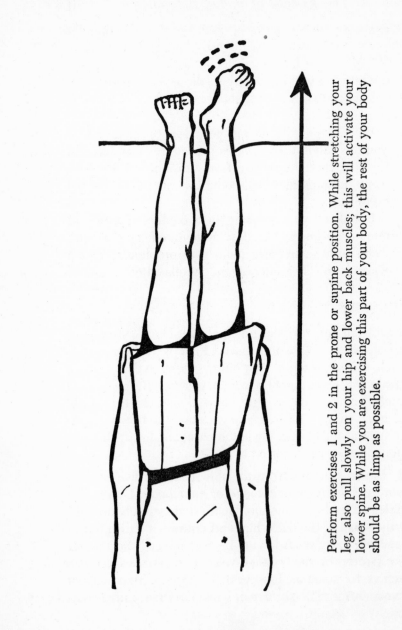

Perform exercises 1 and 2 in the prone or supine position. While stretching your leg, also pull slowly on your hip and lower back muscles; this will activate your lower spine. While you are exercising this part of your body, the rest of your body should be as limp as possible.

FORTABLE REPOSE. REST FOR ABOUT TWO MINUTES OR LONGER. HOLD THE THOUGHT OF "QUIET" IN MIND.

2. Stretch down your *lower left side,* small of the back, hip, and entire leg, down to your spread-out toes. Follow the same instructions as above (No. 1).

3. Stretch upward the *right side of your chest and arm* to the fingertips. Do not be in haste. Then slowly and resistantly pull back your arm and place it alongside your body. The slight stretch should be felt between the ribs, throughout the upper arm, forearm, and fingers. Repeat this several times. Then wriggle your muscles into ease. Rest for two minutes, holding the thought of "quiet" in mind.

4. Stretch up the *left side of your chest and arm* to the fingertips. *Take it slow and easy.* Follow directions above. Then wriggle your muscles into ease. Rest for two minutes, holding the thought of "quiet" in your mind.

5. Slowly stretch your *neck toward the right shoulder;* then *toward the left shoulder,* and pull it back to a normal position. Rest. Slowly stretch your *neck toward your chest,* and then *toward* your back (with your chin up), and gradually pull it back to its normal position. Shake your head into ease. Be sure to rest two minutes in utter quietness.

6. *Exercise your jaw muscles.* Slowly open your mouth to the full extent, but *resist opening it* as though your teeth were stuck together with hard taffy. In closing your mouth, again offer slight resistance from all your neck, face, and forehead muscles, as though you were taking a big bite of a very hard apple. Massage away the possible strain produced. Rest for two minutes.

7. Breathe in slowly and deeply; then exhale fully at a much slower rate, slightly forcing all the residual air out of your lungs. Do this several times, while holding the thought of "quiet" uppermost in your mind.

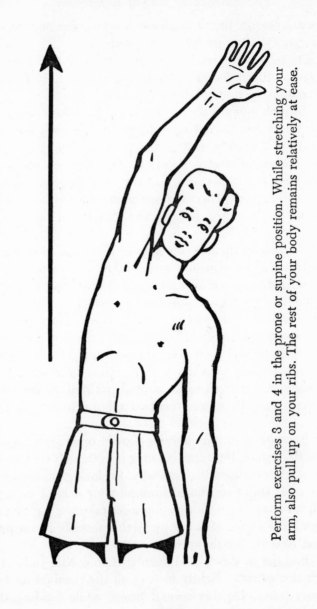

Perform exercises 3 and 4 in the prone or supine position. While stretching your arm, also pull up on your ribs. The rest of your body remains relatively at ease.

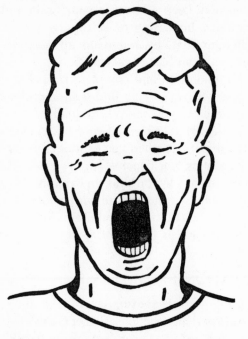

When a yawn is in the making, let it become a finished product. A socially stifled
yawn is of little value. A controlled and
full yawn, as shown above, will activate
all your throat and face muscles.

THE FINAL TOUCH

After the exercises, give yourself whatever additional
support you may need under any part of your body which
may still feel uneasy. This may include placing a soft support under your knees, the calf of your leg near the ankle,
your arms, or the small of your back. Wriggle yourself into
complete ease, and remain that way for as long as you can.
An essential step in relaxation is to place yourself always
in the most comfortable position. Otherwise, the sensations

or irritation may keep activating your brain and nervous system, actually increasing or sustaining your tenseness. Reason dictates that, by removing all possible physical hindrances, you can hasten relaxation.

If you are unable to find complete repose in one given position, you will very likely find it in another. After the stretching exercises, you can relax equally well while resting on the side, front, or back of your body. Do not be discouraged or impatient when you cannot *completely* follow all the instructions, nor become annoyed because you unintentionally move a leg or blink an eyelash. You would be totally unreasonable and unfair with yourself if you expected to learn relaxation immediately. But once learned, it becomes "as easy as falling off a log"—and takes even less effort!

IS RELAXATION EFFORTLESS?

Having followed the exercises of the program, you should now experience the sensation of complete body ease. Make sure that you are as comfortable as possible, and let yourself go. Become absolutely unconcerned and indifferent to everything for the time being. If you are in an "I-don't-care" state of mind, it is sure proof that you have physically relaxed.

Make no more conscious effort to further your relaxation. Effort and relaxation logically and psychologically contradict each other. If distinct effort is maintained, it will defeat its very aim, because it makes for added tenseness.

When you are effortlessly allowing your body to drift more and more into a state of ease, you are entering the true phase of complete physical relaxation. Sense and revel in the greater ease as your body goes deeper and deeper into comfortable repose.

Take for granted that, when you think you are relaxed,

you are not. Therefore continue to become increasingly limp, allowing your muscles to ease more and more, so that your entire body feels just as though you were about to fall asleep. To capture your newly found freedom from tension, your mind should be in that border state of half consciousness. Otherwise you do not develop the memory of floating effortlessly into peaceful relaxation.

AVOID "MUSTS"

Remember that your state of complete relaxation should be free and effortless. If you say to yourself, "I must not move," "I must stay relaxed," you are jeopardizing your efforts, and prolonging your learning time. Therefore, have in your mind the regulating idea, "I *AM* NOW AT EASE."

Recall some delightful experience in which you fully participated and after which you were restfully spent and thoroughly at ease. You simply did not want to move. Then you did not have to command yourself to be limp. Be that way now. Sink into a mood where you will not want to talk, or move your body, or shake your head, or move a hand or finger. Show no sign of wakefulness; although fully awake, lie perfectly motionless, so that an onlooker would assume that you are peacefully asleep. Take moderately full and rhythmic breaths. Sense your state of muscular well-being and freedom, and above all, be at peace with yourself and the world. If you are afraid of forgetting some important matter that comes to your consciousness, rouse yourself far enough to make a note of it for future reference.

DON'T GO TO SLEEP!

Hold the thought in mind that you do not want to fall asleep, that you want to experience the full effect of your power to relax all your muscles. If you have an assistant, let him repeat the same thought in a soothing, calm voice.

This will have the effect of making you more and more relaxed.

When you are relaxed thoroughly, you are conscious of everything that goes on; but you have determined not to be responsive to anything. You are willingly at complete rest. Of your own volition, you act as though you were asleep, knowing that at a moment's notice, you can become wide awake.

Keep your eyes open, especially at the beginning of the relaxation procedure. It is most important to remain awake, although you should not force yourself to do so. What should you do if you are really very tired? Take a short nap. When you awake, start all over again. Of course, as you become more and more relaxed, your eyes may close automatically.

Under prolonged expert care, you can become completely relaxed through physical relaxation alone. But if you consciously use the combined simple methods of this book, you can achieve the ends of thorough relaxation yourself, without professional supervision.

HOW LONG SHALL I REST?

Generally speaking, you may remain in the relaxed position for as long as time permits or you find it comfortable to do so. With training, you may learn to lie completely motionless for an hour. But if you should be able to rest no more than seven to twenty-five minutes without stirring, do not be discontented with your efforts. You would then merely be imitating the usual time which, experiments have shown, a normal person sleeps without stirring or moving.

DANGERS OF PROLONGED RELAXATION

Relaxation is the fundamental basis for the time-honored rest cure. Nevertheless, *too prolonged rest also has a weak-*

ening effect. Hence the necessity for balancing it with some activity. Do not permit yourself to become *over*relaxed. Your muscles need to be in *tone.* Muscle tone may be compared to the elasticity or resiliency of rubber. Those who become inactive and do not use their muscles lose that tone. They become flabby, tire easily, and simply haven't the muscle power to continue with their regular daily activities.

If you relax too much, you become flabby in mind as well as in body. When a person is sick in bed for a long time, mental alertness as well as the healing and restorative powers are hindered. All bodily processes are slowed down by a lack of oxygen in the blood. Modern surgery, recognizing this fact, has made a complete about-face by encouraging the patient to get out of bed the first or second day after a major operation.

Remember that your body should be used; the more fruitfully it is used, the stronger you become in every respect. Short periods of relaxation increase its efficiency by following the natural law of rhythmic and cyclical rest.

TESTS FOR RELAXATION CAPACITY

Now, let us examine what you have accomplished by your first period of relaxation. Check on how you felt before you started to relax (see page 29).

1. As you rest now, attempt to lift your arm or leg—does it feel heavy? Is it an effort for you to do so? If the limb feels very light, you may be certain that you have not sufficiently relaxed. You need more time and practice. After all, *relaxation is an art and cannot be learned in a few minutes.* Make yourself feel heavier until you experience the sensation of being completely limp. You will notice that your body becomes heavier as you increase the depth of relaxation, which is a sure sign that it has taken its full effect.

2. Recall whether you had minor bodily annoyances before you started to relax. Are they lessened now? If the irritations didn't leave you, it shows that you didn't relax well; it may also mean that the minor irritations have a deep origin which needs professional care. You cannot overcome all your irritations through your own efforts alone.

3. Are you as sensitive to noises or environmental disturbances after a period of relaxation as you were before? Do the children yell as loud as before? Does the dog bark as loud? Does the telephone ring as harshly? Is the door squeak as annoying? When you become thoroughly relaxed, you will be aware of an appreciable difference in the quality or apparent intensity of sound, for the simple reason that, as fatigue lessens, noises are not so distracting.

4. Is your mind quieter? A sure test of your success with this method is when your thinking quiets down. If worries are still uppermost in your thoughts, it indicates that you have only experienced superficial relaxation. *The deeper your body gets into the state of repose, the quieter your mind becomes.*

5. Are your emotions under control? If your period of relaxation was at all successful, it should have the effect of quieting whatever emotional turbulence you may have had. If your mood didn't change, it signifies what a strong hold the emotions have on your mind and body. With continued periods of repose, you can gain better control of your moods. To learn this skill of relaxation, as with all other accomplishments, requires time, patience, and perseverance.

6. Another important test of your success with relaxation is if your eyes feel more at ease after than before the period of your repose. There should be a distinct difference in the way your eyes feel. The elimination of tension in your eyes is most difficult to accomplish, and by the same token, most

beneficial when achieved. Follow through with the suggestions given in the next chapter.

Realize that the calmness which you radiate will have its influence not only upon your own functioning, but also upon those who need your help.

ABBREVIATED FORM OF RELAXATION

After about ten or more sessions of our extensive program of exercises and relaxation, your muscles have been strengthened, and you may be sufficiently trained and prepared to use this abbreviated form of relaxation. It does away with counting, and with exercising individual parts of your body. The chief skill involved is the ability to use the controlled and resistant stretch and the pull back of your muscles. Do not allow your muscles to become strained through excess ambition of quick mastery. Learn to let go of your entire body after the exercises. Be sure to wriggle yourself out of the stretch. Quiet your mind through the use of the symbolic word "quiet."

1. Now, choose a bed, a couch, or a blanket on the floor.
2. Loosen all restraining articles of clothing, including collars, bras, belts, garters, compressing hose and shoes.
3. Allot a *minimum* of ten minutes and give instructions not to be disturbed, so that you can rest with an easy mind.
4. Lie on your back. Perform the slow easy stretching exercises of all your muscles at one time, just as one does or should do upon arising. This would necessarily include stretching the muscles of your jaws, arms, legs, back, chest, abdomen, and neck. Avoid snapping your muscles back in the sharp staccato "one-two" schooldays fashion. The rule is: *always stretch your muscles slowly, against resistance, and pull them back equally slowly to a comfortable position.*

5. WRIGGLE OR SHAKE YOUR BODY OUT OF THE STRETCH INTO A POSITION OF EASE.

A BASIC RULE: USUALLY YOUR MUSCLES ARE NOT RELAXED WHEN YOU THINK THEY ARE. THEREFORE, KEEP ON EASING THEM UP MORE AND MORE TO A STATE OF LIMPNESS.

6. Remember, you may place additional support under any part of your body if it helps to produce a greater amount of repose.

7. Your head and neck must be placed comfortably on the pillow to avert a pull on your scalp muscles. This makes it easier for you to relax your eyes. This eye relaxation is so important that you should perform the eye exercises to be given in the next chapter.

8. Control your breathing so that it is slow, regular, and rhythmic.

9. Now commence to use the word "quiet." By the persistent use of the word "quiet," you send down mental messages to further ease up any part of your body which failed to relax. Use this same word to bring greater tranquillity within your mind. Remain in the state of relaxation for as long as your time permits.

10. When finally your body is in complete repose, become fully aware that you have within you a *reservoir* of intuitive wisdom, power, endurance, and strength to cope with your problems. This comforting spiritual awareness involves a full appreciation of your real capabilities, plus a sense that you are playing some useful role in the total scheme of things.

Carry over your newly gained freedom from tension into all your endeavors.

5.

How to Relax the Eyes

PHYSICAL EYE EXERCISES · FOR A TOTAL REST
MENTAL EYE VACATIONS · NOW SMILE

THE eye is so intimately connected with the brain and nervous system that it not only reflects the entire gamut of our emotions, but also mirrors the state of health, disease, and nervous tension of the body and the mind.

Of all the muscles that must be relaxed, those of the eye are the most important. When they are in a state of perfect repose, the rest of your body will more readily be at ease, and your emotions will be under better control. When your eyes and face muscles are completely relaxed, you simply cannot worry! Eye relaxation not only is an aid in obtaining rested nerves, but it also helps to achieve a charming and friendly look.

Any strain to the human being can cause eye tension. Thus, all measures that can influence our general health need to be utilized. A helpful procedure is to temporarily lay aside the tasks facing you by making memos. The mere listing of them may ease your mind.

PHYSICAL EYE EXERCISES

A few minutes of the following exercises will ease up the six muscles that control the movement of the eye. *Use them for general relaxation, or whenever your eyes become tired or strained. Rest or exercise your eyes occasionally while working, studying, reading, playing, watching television or 3-D movies.*

Perform these exercises in a sitting or lying position. Eye exercises can be done *in two separate and distinct ways,* as shown in the table below:

1. By moving your head in the directions indicated.
2. By keeping your head still and only moving your eyes.

A. Look five or more times in each direction.

B. Avoid strain. Perform all movements slowly and easily.

C. Continue for a few minutes. Rest when tired.

1. Look up and down.
2. Look to the right and to the left.
3. Look to the right corner of the ceiling, to the left corner of the floor.
4. Look to the left corner of the ceiling, to the right corner of the floor.
5. Roll your eyes slowly in large circles, then in very small circles, clockwise and counterclockwise.
6. Look straight ahead far into the distance, then shift your eyes by looking at an object immediately close to you.
7. Tighten your eyes as though avoiding strong sunlight, and then open them very gradually. Avoid frowning. Make sure that your eye muscles become perfectly at ease.

Very likely the muscles of your jaws, lips, upper part of the nose, the forehead, temples, or the scalp may still be taut. Several extensive yawns can be helpful. In addition, massage the face and forehead as though you were washing them.

Pressure on the forehead will also give relief to tired eyes. If you have difficulty in relaxing your eyes while lying on your back try this procedure. Lace your fingers together. Place your palms on your forehead. Slightly gather the skin of your forehead. Let the weight of the hands be toward your eyes, and not toward the back of your head. Your hands should be so braced by the lacing of your fingers that they do not separate. Let your elbows fall back on the bed. Thus your forehead receives the full weight of your hands.

For relief from a burning sensation in the eyes, apply a wet cloth over them, and cover with a small towel.

FOR A TOTAL REST

Sit at a table or desk; place your elbows on the table. Put a small pillow or pad under the elbows, so you will be comfortable in this position for a longer time. If no such support is handy, place your elbows on your thighs, above the kneecaps (there is normally a slight depression into which your elbows can fit nicely). Keep your feet about eighteen inches apart; thus you will be anchored and can't fall over. Loosen all tight garments. Bend forward from your hip joints; keep the spine fairly straight.

Have the palms of your hands face you, keeping fingers close together. Place the fingers of one hand at right angles over the fingers of the other hand. Cup your palms. In this position, place the palms over the eyes. There should be no pressure on nor contact with the eyeballs. Your nose should be free from pressure. The heel of your palm (the part nearest your wrist) will be under your cheekbones. Shift your hands, if necessary, until *all* light is excluded.

Stay in this comfortable position as long as you can (see illustration).

MENTAL EYE VACATIONS

With your eyes closed, use *any one* of the following means of temporarily freeing your mind from fatigue, worries, or problems of the moment. The slightest release from your anxieties is a gain to your mental well-being.

1. Take a short "mental vacation" to the most soothing or comforting scene or place that you can recall or imagine.

2. Visualize a familiar black or deep blue object, such as a black shoe, curtain, or hat.

3. Open your eyes. Take a prolonged look at any particular object in your room. It doesn't matter what it may be. Then close your eyes and cover them with your hands—visualize shape, size, color, texture, position, and operation of the object—just as though you were going to buy or pick out an exact match for it. (Visualization, like imagination, requires no effort or mental strain.)

4. Open your eyes; dwell for a minute upon a soothing picture that may be on the wall. Then close your eyes and cover them with your hands. Now allow your mind to become completely absorbed in the picture. In your imagina-

tion, perhaps you may grasp its "message," wondering why the picture was produced. Imagine something about the artist's life, or personality.

NOW SMILE

Sit up straight. Put a happy smile on your face. The smile must not be one implying excitable expectancy. It should be produced by thinking of a pleasant event which will evoke in you a calming and soothing sensation. Keep smiling, and as you do, let the feeling of the smile spread throughout your entire body. You may note a gradual feeling of well-being and ease permeating all through you, even down to your toes. If the smile does not come readily, try to recall an incident in your life when you were pleasantly surprised, or think of your favorite joke. Recall your delight in witnessing a beautiful scene, or think back to some pleasant, and satisfying event.

Now try this: Think of something unpleasant, and note how strain and tension set in immediately, especially in your eyes. Now attempt the impossible—try to produce a happy smile with your teeth clenched and your eyes wide open!

In contrast, note what happens when you are smiling pleasantly and in a relaxed manner. Your teeth are slightly apart, your nostrils are somewhat dilated, and your eyes are partly closed. Every muscle of your face is at ease. The expression will inevitably match the pattern of the correlated experience which brings the smile to your face. It can have a definite although temporary influence upon your whole being.

6.

Relax While Sitting, Standing, and Walking

TO RELAX SITTING · HOW TO SIT
FREEWHEELING · HOW DO YOU WALK?
ADVANTAGES OF RELAXATION

PERHAPS by this time you are wondering how you can relax when it is not convenient nor possible for you to assume a reclining position? Well, you can relax also in other positions and turn your spare minutes into a period of complete rest. But repose is not possible unless your muscles are in tone, hence certain "background" exercises are of primary importance. They will activate your body in preparation for relaxation.

You can also use any of the following simplified exercises to obtain temporary relief from pain in any part of your body, such as the neck, back, arms, or legs. When a part of your body is uneasy or "tied up," rub or massage it slightly until some of the distress is eliminated. Or use home remedies, such as heat or cold. Then relaxation will have more nearly the desired effect on you.

TO RELAX SITTING

Our muscular bodies, flabby from nonuse and excessive sitting, need periodic relaxation. It will be more complete and beneficial if the body is exercised freely for a few minutes. Note which particular part of your body is tense and tired, then stretch that part slowly in every direction.

The same rules and words of caution for exercising in the reclining position (Chapter 4) apply to any other position your body may be in. S-t-r-e-t-c-h to the slow count of five, and pull your muscles back to the same count. Do all your exercises with slow grace and ease. You are doing this not for the purpose of building powerful muscles, but to make them more supple, and to *free* them from their habitual tenseness. By exercising rhythmically and consciously, you will soon establish a systematic habit.

1. Practice taking gentle rhythmic slow breaths, allowing your entire abdomen to rise and fall very slowly and gently. Breathe in easily to the slow count of five; then let the air escape from your lungs even more slowly. Pause a moment before you breathe in again. Slow, rhythmic breathing has a tendency to quiet your emotions.

2. Imitate the controlled yawn and squint your eyes at the same time. Resistantly allow your jaws to close. Full and deep yawning has many functions, among which is the lessening of mental fatigue.

3. Stretch up your right hand, arm, and the right side of your body, making yourself tall. At the same time, take a full breath, as explained above. Slowly, resistantly release those muscles to the normal position. Wriggle the exercised part. Perform the same exercise with your left arm and the left side of your body. Rest for two minutes. This will take you out of a slump, and activate your chest and arm muscles.

4 (*a*). Place the fingers on the inner part of your wrist and forearm. Your palms should fit closely together. Push gently, pressing them together firmly until slight strain can be felt in the shoulders and neck.

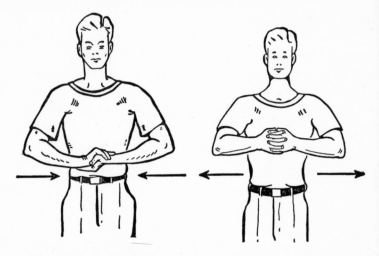

(*b*). Interlock the fingers of each hand, palms facing you. Then pull them away until you can feel the stretch in your shoulder blades. Perform a clockwise and counterclockwise rotation of the shoulders; then rotate the shoulders front and back—a splendid exercise for removing tension between the shoulders.

5. Stretch out your right hip and leg parallel with the chair, holding your abdomen up and in. Time it to the slow count of five for the stretch, and the same for the resistant release to the normal position. Wriggle the exercised part. Perform the same complete exercise with the left hip and leg. This exercise will remove tension in your calf and leg muscles.

6. With your feet together on the floor, stretch and separate your thighs, and then resistantly bring your knees

together. If you are sitting up straight, you should feel the muscular action through your legs and hips, as well as through the lower part of your back and abdomen. Your abdomen should be flattened and not protruding during this process. Try this exercise for strengthening as well as for easing the thigh, hip, and buttocks.

7. Sit with both feet on the ground. Make believe you are picking up marbles with your toes and resistantly letting them drop again on the floor. This is a proved exercise for strengthening the thigh muscles and arches.

8. Stretch your body to the right, then to the left, then

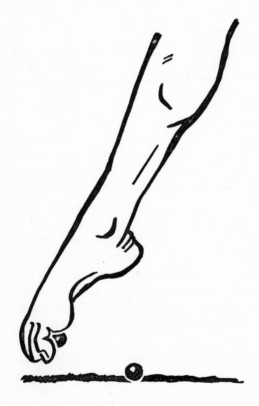

slowly pull back to the normal position. This relieves minor tensions of the lower back muscles.

9. Stretch down with your hands toward the floor and resistantly pull yourself back to normal position. Bend backward and slowly straighten up. This will release some of your imbedded upper back tensions.

10. Stretch your neck to the right, to the left, forward and back for a few minutes. Then wriggle your head a bit. This is good for easing the muscle tension from your neck.

HOW TO SIT

Now that you have exercised, your relaxation in a sitting position will be more complete. You can stay comfortable longer and feel stronger if you *allow your spinal column to carry the weight of your body as intended.* Sit somewhat more forward and balance yourself so that the full body *weight is distributed evenly* throughout the spinal column, not sagging forward or backward, or to one side or the other. (If you are sitting in a straight-backed chair, you may support your spine against it slightly.) Thus you obtain the maximum amount of freedom from muscle strain and fatigue, and can hold the position for a long time.

Such "erectness" is not a fetish but a logical consequence of natural skeletal construction. Your feet should be flat on the floor, and the entire weight of your legs upon them. If you get into the habit of crossing your legs, sitting sideways, tilting your head, or tightening your arms across your chest, you soon tire. Do not try to relax in such a strained position that you constantly have to shift, getting yourself more and more tense and tired. You will not find the expected comfort by crossing your legs and straining still another set of muscles.

Your arms and hands should rest fully in your lap, on the arms of the chair, or on a desk. Your head is evenly balanced on the neck; shoulders are not raised. There should be perfect ease of movement of your head to and fro and from side to side. This will tend to produce the least amount of neck-muscle strain or fatigue.

When you are evenly balanced, not sagging to either side, you can easily get yourself into a state of relaxation. Even if you are only resting for ten minutes, that may be sufficient to take some of the strain off your nerves, and relieve you of a measure of fatigue. Now, to hasten your effortless relaxation, start to practice quietude of mind.

You can practice this correct way of sitting whether at work, at the theater, watching television, listening to the radio, or in the presence of others. By conscientious and repetitious performance, you form the habit. You will no longer sit in the usual contorted and taut fashion, but find it easier to sit gracefully and in perfect repose. If in addition you smile, you will noticeably enhance your grace and radiance. Keep the idea of "quiet" uppermost in your mind. Direct the thought of quiet to every part of your body, especially to your eyes, and to the depths of your consciousness.

FREEWHEELING

Consider how a "freewheeling" or easily balanced standing posture can help you. Good posture will not only make you feel better, but look better too. A balanced body carriage is indicative of your actual well-being and ability to do things efficiently and gracefully.

Good posture is important. Adopt the evenly balanced freewheeling posture, distributing your weight *equally* on *both* feet (which should be in well-fitted, comfortable shoes). Also, be sure that your hips do not protrude and that your abdomen does not sag. Your ribs are not sunk, nor yet held too high. Your shoulders are not so far forward as to cause slouchiness, nor so far back as to produce strain on the chest muscles. Neither are the shoulders "squared" or forced upward, giving a rigid, statuelike appearance.

Your head is best carried evenly balanced on your neck. Your chin is not drooping forward and downward on your chest (making you appear anxious and depressed); nor is your head tilted too far backward, with your nose in the air, giving the impression of looking down upon the world.

If you stand in such a way that only *part* of your muscular and skeletal frame carries the *entire* burden, that part under strain soon becomes tired. Much compensatory shifting and twisting takes place, inevitably resulting in general fatigue.

A poor posture is not only unattractive but it predisposes you to many ills. For example, your eyes may become listless, you wear a haggard facial expression, your head droops on your chest. Your chest sinks, and your ribs compress. Your breathing is hampered, and your circulation is diminished. Your abdomen may protrude, your stomach will drop, your pelvis will tip, and your arches will weaken. Your joints, being slightly distorted, are subject to becoming stiff and rusty (a frequent cause of arthritis). An imbalanced and unattractive posture can produce strains in your muscles and spinal joints; in turn these anatomical distortions can set up irritations to the spinal nerve fibers and blood vessels that permeate all the muscles and structures of your body. And these irritations interfere with nerve impulses. Often this condition may be the remoter basis for physical as well as mental illness.

A slouchy posture suggests that you are depressed. Too rigid or stiff a carriage shows either social aloofness or internal tenseness. *You can actually change your state of emotions by changing your posture!* The reciprocal influence of the two is one of the A-B-C's of psychology.

By becoming aware of, correcting, and controlling your posture, you will fruitfully conserve your energy, and can better carry on all your activities. When you are standing upright, you give the impression of well-being. Now confirm this impression by allowing your eyes to light up and relax your face in a pleasant expression. It is rightly said that no one has finished dressing until he has put on a smile.

To maintain good posture once attained, and to raise your spirits as well, find time for any necessary corrective aid, for periods of relaxation, and for some physical exercise in one form or another.

HOW DO YOU WALK?

Walking, when properly performed, is considered the most natural, easy, and healthful exercise. But observe the people as they walk past you, and you will see that most of them look gloomy or worried, hold their bodies rigid, and appear strained and awkward.

The secret of healthful walking is to permit the entire body to be limber enough so that no part of it is held rigid. We should experience the sensation of body freedom, of ease. The proper position of the body in walking is slightly forward, as though being pushed ahead by a wind. Toes are pointed straight ahead; the knee is lifted slightly with every step. This starts the natural springiness to your walk, which is carried through to the hip joints and all the joints of the spine. This activates all the muscles attached to the skeletal frame. The body rocks and rotates slightly with every step, and with every gentle swing of the arms. Such walking can be continued for a considerable time without fatigue, and it gives one a sense of well-being. As you walk, feel as though you are temporarily leaving your troubles behind you.

ADVANTAGES OF RELAXATION

1. If you relax when excited, your nerves will start to quiet down.

2. Your voice will become more controlled.

3. Clearer thinking will restrain you from fast, excited, thoughtless talking.

4. If you are under pressure from others, you will be better able to disregard any rebuff.

5. If the voices coming in your direction are gruff or loud, relaxation will remind you to offer up a prayer that the speakers may hear themselves as others hear them.

6. If you are hearing words of wisdom, it will increase your capacity to listen and remember.

7. The minutes you devote to relaxation will increase your calmness when waiting "to be next" in any kind of line.

7.

Achieving and Maintaining Physical Fitness

WHERE DOES YOUR ENERGY COME FROM?
DAILY REGIMEN · THE BREATH OF LIFE
YOUR DIET · YOUR NEED FOR WATER
YOUR HEALTH RESTS UPON YOUR FEET
RHYTHMIC EXERCISES · THE DAILY DOZEN VARIETY
EMOTIONAL VALUE OF PHYSICAL EXERCISE
BATHING FOR RELAXATION · SLEEP
YOUR FACE—THE MIRROR OF YOUR EMOTIONS
THE IMPORTANCE OF LAUGHTER
LAUGHTER WITHOUT HUMOR

THE first requisite for prolonged effort of any kind is physical strength. The better your state of health, the greater your efficiency. Lacking energy, all your acquired knowledge, intuitive wisdom, and genuine desire to succeed, will avail but little. *With a properly relaxed body and mind,* these other valuable attributes are cementing influences acting to assure your success. Furthermore, good health is the indispensable foundation to all emotional well-being.

WHERE DOES YOUR ENERGY COME FROM?

Your energy depends upon the ability of your body to absorb, transport, and utilize fresh air, wholesome food, and pure water. In order to do so, you require above all else:

1. A well co-ordinated brain and nervous system, free from all irritations and interferences.

2. A properly functioning breathing apparatus and digestive system.

3. An unhindered circulatory system to move blood and other body fluids.

4. Unimpaired systems of elimination, through the skin, lungs, and excretory organs.

5. An evenly balanced, smoothly functioning glandular system.

6. Good body posture.

7. Emotional stability and capacity to cope with all sorts of frustrations.

8. Awareness that you possess a spark of universal energy, the basic part-whole relation in Nature which makes all things possible.

To conserve your energy, live zestfully, but don't waste your strength needlessly. Lessen the amount and vigor of talking, sit whenever possible instead of standing, and even lie down when convenient instead of sitting. Time taken out to acquire maximum energy or preserve your general health is never time lost. In your daily schedule of activities, you *must* allot definite periods for promoting physical revitalization.

DAILY REGIMEN

The establishing of a daily regimen for physical betterment should not be regarded as a hardship, nor should the rules prove distressingly difficult to obey. If you acquire the habit of abiding by your new daily schedule, you will quickly notice its beneficial effects. It becomes just as easy for you to eat, drink, breathe, etc., in the new better way.

An easy way to follow your new schedule of healthful living is to combine it with some of your well-established habits. For instance, associate washing your face with the habit of deep breathing, and drink a glass or two of water. While dressing, establish the habit of lightly exercising your body at the same time. When changing your clothes, if there is no time for bathing, rub your skin briskly with your hands or with a Turkish towel. When you make notes of the different things to do for your home or your job, also place on that list a reminder to take care of *your own* immediate health needs, such as rest, recreation, exercise, and deep breathing.

THE BREATH OF LIFE

Breathing is always affected by anxiety or emotional strain. When you are fatigued or depressed, inhalation is usually very shallow. This deprives your entire body of the full quota of oxygen. Lack of oxygen in the brain increases depression. Thus a vicious cycle sets in through continued shallow respiration alone. It is therefore evident that *deep* and *rhythmic* breathing should become habitual with you.

Rhythmic breathing means imitating the normal breathing that takes place while you're asleep. To produce rhythmic breathing consciously, allow it to be free, full, easy, and slow. Of itself, it can have a calming influence on you. This is one easy way to cope with depression.

Fresh air is a *first* requisite for general good health. Vigor of body, as well as clear thinking, depends upon inhaling a goodly quantity of fresh air. Open your windows at suitable intervals to ventilate your room thoroughly. Inhale deeply for several minutes to eliminate all stagnant air from your lungs. Practice slowly any exercise you wish, such as moving your arms up and down, or bending backward and forward. Practice deep breathing while standing, sitting, walking, or in a lying position. When the habit is well established, you will breathe deeply and rhythmically without thinking about it. Do not however attempt to start suddenly and overdo this regime of deep breathing. Develop it gradually.

YOUR DIET

Seek dietary advice from your doctor to avoid nutritional mistakes that can endanger your health.

In general these are the basic foods that you can depend upon: Whole wheat bread and other whole-grain products (unless you are troubled by an intestinal condition); certified milk, and milk products; fresh vegetables and fruits; beef, glandular meats; some fish; eggs; honey or brown sugar for sweetening. Foods to avoid: commercial white bread; white flour products, which includes most cakes; white sugars and their products; excessive amounts of condiments and spices.

Vary your daily diet. If most of your work is indoors, you don't need as much food as when you are doing strenuous outside work. In any event, the *quality* of your food is always more important than the *quantity*, once that is above a certain absolute minimum. Observe for yourself which particular foods are or are not easy for you to digest. Does coffee drinking distress you or cause biliousness? Some people cannot tolerate tea, yet it has no noticeable effect on others. If, in your experience, these beverages cause no digestive or nervous irritability you need not abstain. If you suspect that they may be affecting you adversely, eliminate either coffee or tea, or any article of food for a short period of time, and then observe the effects upon you.

For quick energy or "pick-up," try using a lemon-and-honey drink, or a raw egg beaten up in orange juice. If subject to gastro-intestinal distress, avoid taking liquids with your meals.

Whenever possible, *eat in a quiet place.* Conversation, if any, should always be pleasant or neutral—never controversial. Emotional disturbances definitely reduce the stomach secretions of gastric juice and interfere with digestion. If there is any unpleasantness at the dining table, or if the table setting or the preparation of the food is not quite to your liking, remember that the nourishment (as well as the good will of your companions) is so necessary for you that you must concentrate all your thoughts on the food and enjoy it anyway. When your thoughts are upon the need for the food, then the other inconveniences or "trimmings" become secondary.

Discover for yourself whether you feel best by relaxing before or after eating, or if it is better for you to do some walking or work at these times. People vary greatly in this respect, depending on age and other conditions. When your experience clearly indicates which procedure is best for you, follow it.

YOUR NEED FOR WATER

Your body is composed of about 67 per cent water; thus water in a certain sense can be considered as a "food." There is also an emotional reason for drinking enough water. As it lessens your brain congestion, it thus slightly lessens your anxiety about pressing problems. While it does not lessen your actual mental distress, water helps to free your body of the various toxins generated through emotional upheavals, poisons which, if they remain in your blood stream, set up irritations that interfere with the smooth functioning of the nervous system.

Water dissolves hardened debris in your body tissues and blood stream; it picks up the useless worn-out particles, and carries them away. It reduces excess acids, and brings circulation up to par. It is a natural stimulant, a cleansing agent, an equalizer of your circulation, a solvent and eliminator of the broken-down and worn-out body cells.

Unless a condition exists (usually cardiac) which makes it inadvisable for you to take too much water, you should drink a minimum of six to eight glasses of it a day.

So much for food and drink. Now we come to another important prerequisite for well-being.

YOUR HEALTH RESTS UPON YOUR FEET

If you consider your body as a machine, the very first thing that any machine requires is a *level* base! Therefore, pay attention to your feet. Your posture depends primarily upon the condition of your feet. Poorly placed feet, fallen arches, or ill-fitting shoes, will soon create fatigue, and your health will suffer.

When your superimposed body structure bears down upon your weakened arches, it will make your feet weaker. It will also fatigue your nerves, and your "understanding" will suffer—physically, as well as mentally! If you have *fallen* arches, as distinct from merely *low* arches which may be quite normal, your doctor will tell you what to do about them, such as: soaking tired feet in hot water, then in cold water, followed by friction or massage. He may also recommend exercises (such as trying to pick up marbles with your toes), or perhaps he will tell you to wear arch supports (see page 51).

RHYTHMIC EXERCISES

In performing rhythmic exercises for relaxation, use the usual exercises designed for toughening muscles, *but keep your muscles limp and relaxed.* Instead of bending strenuously to touch your toes, let your body drop loosely.

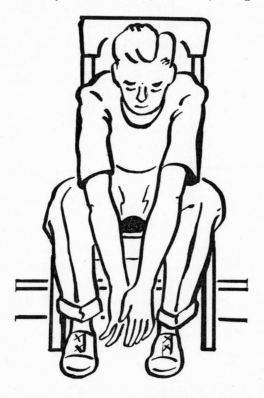

Instead of lifting your arms up as though they were weighted down, lift them as though they were light as feathers. Twist your body from side to side, letting it fall without effort (as you would shake a soft rag doll). Roll your head from side to side, and drop it back and forward, making it limp, as though you had no control over it. This important difference in the *way* you exercise determines the result.

THE DAILY DOZEN VARIETY

Exercise your body to keep *all* your major muscles strong, supple, and active, and to prevent them from shortening or pulling in an uneven direction. Always exercise in a room with the windows open. If you are subject to colds, close the door to avoid drafts.

Of course, *the best exercise is walking*. A long walk in the open is a combination of recreation, relaxation, and free and complete body movement. If you are too fatigued, do not fight it. First take a short sleep or rest, and then go for your regular walk.

Your daily work cannot be considered as true exercise, because in working, we do not ordinarily use *all* our muscles.

EMOTIONAL VALUE OF PHYSICAL EXERCISE

Among all the beneficial physical effects that exercise produces, you should be particularly aware that through it you will be able to work off the glandular energy generated by excess or strong emotions such as fear and anger, as well as disturbing erotic sensations. When people and situations upset you, go for a walk. This is much more satisfying than shouting, moping, plotting revenge, or other inappropriate reactions.

BATHING FOR RELAXATION

When you get up in the morning, zestfully wash your face, neck, shoulders, and arms with cold water.

Bathing is even more useful in cleansing the soul than in washing the skin. When you are unduly fatigued or disturbed, if you haven't the opportunity to "walk it off" or "talk it off," you will usually find it soothing, refreshing, and relaxing to take a hot bath.

For purposes of relaxation, stay in *hot* water for about fifteen minutes; longer, if you are not too uncomfortable. (However, if you are extremely fatigued do not make the water too hot—it may be too exhausting.) Drink a glass or two of cold water or fruit juice while in the tub and place a cold towel on your forehead. When drying yourself, don't rub your skin too briskly but gently pat yourself dry, and then rest a while in bed.

SLEEP

Of course, no form of activity is a substitute for plenty of sleep. Your health may not suffer if occasionally you don't get your usual amount of sleep, but its continued lack will definitely show in your mental attitude and your re-action to irritations. Sleep is the one great antidote for fatigue, and the restorer of energy.

YOUR FACE—THE MIRROR OF YOUR EMOTIONS

You may be unable to keep your emotions from show-ing in your face, but proper care of it will at least guarantee you an expression of freshness and alertness.

Applying a cold towel to your face, then a hot towel, alternating several times, will remove much of your facial tiredness. In applying hot and cold towels, apply the heat for about two minutes and the cold for half a minute. This method helps to increase the circulation, freshens your skin, and acts as a mild general tonic.

Soothe your eyes by applying a cold pack; then cover up your eyes with a dry napkin, and relax for a few minutes. The cold will remove much of the congestion and "burn-ing" sensation from your eyes. *If you want to appear to feel well, you must look well.* This is not a question of beauty; it's a solemn necessity.

THE IMPORTANCE OF LAUGHTER

Laughter is a combination of relaxation, recreation, and exercise. The experience of well-being that follows a good hearty laugh is not only pleasant but has far-reaching and long-lasting functional importance to both mind and body.

Cheerfulness is a tonic. You can at least create an authentic smile on your face, and let it penetrate into your soul. If you can't think of anything humorous, or read or hear anything funny, *laugh at yourself, especially when over-whelmed by your feelings of self-importance.* Look yourself straight in the eye and utter a lusty, "Haw, haw, haw!" This will do for you something that nothing else will. Be glad that you have the power to laugh, and grateful that your worst worries didn't materialize.

LAUGHTER WITHOUT HUMOR

Have you ever noticed that even when you laugh out of sheer politeness you end up feeling better? The actual muscular motions of laughter give your spirits a lift. Try the following exercises for a full minute:

1. Breathe in and out very quickly in spasmodic staccato fashion.
2. Move your abdomen up and down and in and out rapidly.
3. Move your shoulders up and down jerkily.
4. Rock your head up and down very slightly.
5. Keep your mouth open.
6. Have a full, beaming smile on your face.

Now do all these muscular movements at the same time, and see what happens to your low spirits.

Let us analyze why laughter, with or without humor, is so beneficial. As you agreeably rock your entire muscular frame, you activate the diaphragm, heart, lungs, stomach, liver, intestines. You clear the bronchial tubes and nasal passages. The rocking squeezes out a few tears from the eyes. It quickly drains congested blood from the brain, and increases the flow of blood carrying oxygen to the brain. It immediately relieves much of your neuromuscular tension. Is there any wonder why you feel better when you laugh?

8.

Mental Relaxation Through Quietude

THE WORD "QUIET" · CAN YOU REMEMBER . . . ?
A HAUNTING MELODY · MEDITATION

At no time in recorded history has inner quietude been as necessary as it is now. Never before have our brains and nerves been so disturbed by all sorts of loud and exciting sounds. And even if we are not assaulted by noise, we still need quietude to counteract the underlying turmoil that is usually residing deep within us. If we desire to rest both our minds and our bodies, we must possess inner peace.

Some authorities are of the opinion that, when the body is completely relaxed, the mind cannot think; but this is not always true. Observation plus experiment proves that your body may be at ease, yet paradoxically you may be *straining* to keep yourself from thinking! (Like the old saw about the futility of trying to prevent oneself from thinking of the word or image "hippopotamus"—it can't be done.) This is in line with the psycho-dynamics of the subconscious mind. Just as the heart is active even when the body is entirely at rest, so too is the mind.

THE WORD "QUIET"

The most effective method of quieting the mind is to combine physical methods of relaxation with mental suggestion. Clinical evidence has proved that a symbolic word like "quiet" helps to obtain mental relaxation. This "push-button" word, "quiet," is one that we use when we are annoyed with external disturbances. We yell it to a dog, or shout it at a child, or use it to silence anyone else who annoys us. Similarly, we can use it *internally* to still our turbulent minds. At the beginning of the period of relaxation, use the word with emphasis. It should be said as an *inward command* to quiet down all our activity, to be at ease, at rest. Now is the time to do nothing, *absolutely nothing,* with no thought entering our minds. No voluntary muscle should twitch or move.

To use the word "quiet" only occasionally while in the relaxed condition is of little permanent value. Repeat it with every slow exhalation and inhalation. A subvocal use of the word is all that is required. *It is not said audibly*— no one should hear you; but the word should not be kept far in the back of your mind. Instead, keep it in the forefront of your consciousness, right on the tip of your tongue. No vocal muscles are moving; the tongue does not cleave to the roof of the mouth; teeth are slightly separated; but the symbol itself is mentally uppermost. As you continue to employ it, it will increase its forceful effect upon your mind.

But before using the word "quiet" you should first relax your entire muscular system. Still it has been reported by many users of this method that the term "quiet" by itself seems to still the body even before it quiets the mind. If for any reason muscular relaxation is retarded, "quiet" has the effect of accelerating the process of physical relaxation. There are always individual peculiarities in the "conditioning" process. So if you find it difficult or impossible first to relax your muscles, you may hasten relaxation by first quieting your mind. After all, body and mind are one.

In any case, neuromuscular relaxation can fortunately be produced *either* by quieting the mind or by quieting the body. When the entire organism is quieted at the *same* time, *complete* relaxation can be attained more quickly.

Give yourself repeatedly the command of "quiet, quiet." Every other thought is swept away; every other concern disappears. Do not concern yourself with any other person or thing about you. Simply suggest to your entire body and mind to be *quiet* and at ease. Have complete confidence that if the word is *regularly* employed, it will finally have full effect, and by achieving this form of *self-mastery,* you can for the time being hold troubles and worries in abeyance.

Do not attempt to shut out all thought and become a pure gray blank; nor try to induce unconsciousness. Merely give yourself the suggestion of becoming calm and letting everything else go while the restful state alone endures. Become unconcerned about all problems. Pressing affairs can wait. Be neutral in your feelings about all matters. It is immaterial whether your eyes are open or closed, although the latter state commonly occurs.

You will also find much comfort in the following supplementary method.

CAN YOU REMEMBER . . . ?

Forcing oneself or concentrating intensely in an attempt to subdue thoughts may produce *additional* tension. The desired soothing and comforting effect can be obtained by trying to recall some particularly pleasant scene, reminiscent of an incident in happy childhood or youthful travels. To "take a mental vacation" effectively, the scenes chosen should neither be exciting nor exasperating; nor should they be highly stimulating or sensual experiences, thrilling heights of achievement or past successes. The memory should visualize and hold views, such as beautiful land-scapes, which were originally pleasant and calming, and which still have those characteristics.

When such a scene appears upon your broad field of memory, settle comfortably in that particular background. Do not permit your mind to wander outside the frame-work of this canvas to other scenes. For example: You may see a picture of a pleasant clear lake on a warm bright day with the trees in blossom and a soothing breeze blowing. That scene must be *anchored* in the mind, without letting the attention wander away to other fields. As you rest, com-pletely at ease, your mind, if successfully relaxed, keeps dwelling on that particular calming portrait. Do not permit yourself to get away from that quiet-inducing scene, unless another one arises within an *equally* soothing or relaxing framework. No mental effort should be used, as that defeats the entire purpose of relaxation. The memory should come spontaneously. In fact, we cannot *forcibly* remember any-thing. When excess energy is summoned to remember, we invariably block our own objective. The best way to sum-mon back anything that has been forgotten is to *let it alone* and it then tends to emerge spontaneously.

A HAUNTING MELODY

If you find it difficult to recall attractive scenes of the pictorial nature just described, try the next best thing. Pick a melody out of your mental storehouse, and inwardly follow it without humming it to yourself; or select pleasant music on radio or phonograph. Let your thoughts follow the course of that agreeable composition, picturing in your imagination the significance of the notes, chords, phrases, themes, and melodies which are being played.

MEDITATION

Another good method of outwitting our anxieties and quieting our thoughts is *meditation,* which, although it makes use of a method very different from remembering a particular scene, achieves the same result. When your body has assumed a restful and comfortable position, encourage yourself to think of scenes not connected with the immediate environment. *Mentally* step away from the problems facing you. Let your mind wander about like a vagabond, without a care, thoroughly "foot-loose and fancy-free." Envisage a scene in which rain is falling. Thinking about the rain recalls the memory of a waterfall. As the waterfall appears, remembrance of a pleasant rural vacation comes to mind. The memory of the vacation brings back still another occasion, perhaps a pleasant experience on a farm, or a walk along a peaceful country road. Thus the meditation runs one idea smoothly into another.

Now permit your thoughts to come back slowly to your present situation, but *reappraise the entire scene with yourself in it.* After a refreshing period of relaxation and meditation on *other* matters, you may be able to see your current problems *in their right proportions.* The process is something like watching a home motion picture in which you have some part. You see yourself, and you see your relationship to the others involved. Whatever decisions you make after such a period of meditation will be wiser than any you would have made when you were tense.

(1) Music, (2) mental vacations, (3) the use of the word "quiet," (4) meditation are four handy devices for placing yourself in a state of ease and thus freeing yourself from major irritations and annoyances, at least for the time being.

9.

Relaxation Through Suggestion

THE BASES FOR AUTOSUGGESTION
VERBAL REPETITION
HINTS FOR SUCCESSFUL APPLICATION

WE LIVE in a world saturated with the mechanism of suggestion. By radio, television, films, or printed matter, interested persons or groups tell us what to eat and when, what to wear and when, what to drink, how to sleep, where to go and what to think. A large proportion of these suggestions are negative. Sickness, fear, and hate are constantly pursuing us in almost every newspaper or mass periodical, beginning with the front-page headlines and ending in the comics. Evidently we have not yet been completely undermined by this mountain of unhealthy suggestions, otherwise we would all be neurotic!

We do, however, allow adverse suggestions to undermine our health. The marked increase in mental illness, heart trouble, and high blood pressure strongly implies that to some degree at least we talk—or think—ourselves into sickness! Psychiatrists claim that "adverse" thoughts and emotions are responsible for anywhere from 40 to 60 per cent of *all* illness.

73

Not only are we subject to suggestion all our lives, but *we use it continually*. When a mother assures her child that the pain will pass away, or that he can do this or that, she is using suggestion in its most elementary form.

There is power in words. Ideas expressed in words seep into the subconsciousness. When ideas are again and again expressed in appropriate verbal terms and translated into action, we change gradually, just as the earth changes seasonally—and just as strikingly.

For example: once you have mastered the methods of physical relaxation, a change of some fundamental habit has taken place. The achievement of complete body ease is, in itself, a potent demonstration of the nature of suggestion. Instead of being tense and excited, you have learned how to "let go" of your taut muscles and disturbing thoughts, and to replace them with more agreeable substitutes.

To practice *auto*suggestion effectually, you must be thoroughly convinced of the necessity for these suggestions and of your ability to execute them. And you must persist until they take hold in your mind and become habitual, dependable parts of your nature.

But autosuggestion must be based on truth. You should not be blind to unmistakable shortcomings and weaknesses, nor ignore the changes that age or other factors may bring. Merely to suggest to yourself that "I'm well" when you are sick may hinder you from seeking help. To suggest to yourself that you have the capacity to do a truly impossible task may only cause you to become further discouraged and depressed. To say to yourself, "I understand myself completely," when you are in need of insight and self-searching, is again doing yourself an injustice. Strive to uncover the hidden sources of your weaknesses, anxieties, and fears. Recognize that it is usually possible to understand yourself better once you become conscious of these weaknesses.

Autosuggestions based on unreality or plainly impossible tasks are better not even started; they lead only to disaster.

At the same time, holding to the realistic point of view, you can do your best under existing conditions by fully appraising and recognizing the powers within you and putting them to use. Make it your business to emphasize your good points. Do the things you *can* do best.

Suggest to yourself that *it is possible* to obtain whatever you need in the way of motive, skill, or attitude. Give these suggestions to yourself at frequent intervals. By relaxing often, you will soon become aware that you have unused resources of wisdom and strength to draw on.

But guard yourself against inertia. It is the greatest stumbling block that constructive autosuggestion has to overcome. The habit of sheer laziness can masquerade as legitimate physical fatigue. It will keep whispering, "What's the use?" "Don't bother." "Leave it alone." "It can't be done." How much easier it is to make no further effort when you meet with reverses than to try again.

We must also remember that we cannot accomplish anything by hoarding our energy. On the contrary, the more active we are, the stronger we become. Especially in times of crisis when we are on the verge of an achievement, we must move from "I must," to "I can," and finally to "I will" with no debilitating thoughts dragging at our elbows. This is one reason why *continuous* repetitious autosuggestion is so vital.

Without being aware of it, the individual is constantly making to himself suggestions that lead to good or evil, strength or weakness, wisdom or foolishness. The total environment *does* influence us selectively *one way or another*. Hence the importance of *the right choice*. By constantly giving yourself the suggestion of strength, you combat inertia effectively. You become responsive to the situation in which you find yourself at a particular time, and more sensitive and alert to the possibilities of obtaining your objective. You must either assert yourself or permit inertia to overpower you.

The astounding power of suggestion over the human organism can be easily demonstrated. *The person who finds a new interest is full of enthusiasm.* He doesn't permit weaknesses or weariness to subdue him. He forges ahead effortlessly, powered by fresh vigor. Strength comes to him and flows from him.

It is a basic law of nature that the more active we are, the stronger we become. We cannot become strong or stay youthful by saving all of our energy. Thus the periods of relaxation need not be of long duration to be of maximum benefit.

THE BASES FOR AUTOSUGGESTION

1. Formulate into a short, concise sentence the particular mental or physical attribute you need—such as courage, health, strength, opportunity, wisdom, buoyancy, willingness, cheerfulness, etc.; then silently, passively, and in a relaxed manner, repeat that idea over and over again. Do so before going to sleep, upon arising, and at every other convenient occasion. This is not magic, or the incantation of a primitive medicine man, but a demonstrated method of realizing the end you seek.

Autosuggestion is most effective for the comparatively normal person who, by repeating to himself, "I am happy, healthy, and useful" can, with a little extra effort, attain these objectives.

2. Do not be discouraged and cease further effort if your suggestion does not take hold right away. When you first give yourself a suggestion, it may leave as little impression on your mind as your foot leaves on a sandy beach on a

windy day. After the first impression, old waves of thought, like gusts of wind, immediately cover it up. But after the suggestion has been attentively repeated again and again (especially when your conscious thoughts are calmly presented and received), it will sink into your subconscious, making a deep and well-marked "groove" in your mind which shifting or antagonistic thoughts can not so readily obliterate.

Gain little victories daily. Hold on to your long-term dreams but anchor your present goals to the reality of the immediate situation. Evaluate shrewdly all your plans and schemes, relegating to the future the obviously "big" goals, and concentrating now on *moving step-by-step* in little ways if necessary toward the early fulfillment of present possibilities. And, above all, remember that autosuggestion must have for its basis some vital necessity or compelling motive. No suggestion can act with much force if you have an indifferent "take-it-or-leave-it" attitude.

However, when you are overwhelmed by an oppressive problem, to which no solution can be found in a reasonable length of time, do not struggle unceasingly with it. A short period of relaxation or sleep or even some external interruption should break the forced concentration. While in such a relaxed state, or before falling asleep, give yourself the suggestion that upon arising your mind will be clearer, and that somehow your problem will be solved. You will get results with surprising frequency.

At times you may find that the idea of being strong and capable is pushed aside by the unbidden pessimistic thought—"I can't do it; it is hard; I cannot accomplish it; I'm afraid; I'm not trained; I don't know what to do." It is then that you should take counsel from your clear mind. When put to the test, the weakest individual accomplishes things which no one ever believed him capable of doing.

Until we are adequately motivated, we just don't comprehend *how much* we are capable of achieving.

VERBAL REPETITION

To implant an idea into your mind, *the method of verbal repetition at every opportunity is far superior to committing the idea to paper in the form of a resolution.* Such resolutions unfortunately seldom become habits of conduct, perhaps because the act of writing them tends to make *terminal* what should really be only the *initial* process.

Autosuggestion as here interpreted is at bottom a process of learning, and like most learning procedures, is best started with simple objects which do not make too great a demand on one's insight. Just as many of your present elementary habits of thought were formed by repeating a simple idea again and again, the same method can be employed to build *new* habits.

Notice how often a child will say, "I don't like it," or "I can't, I can't," and how as a consequence this idea becomes so fixed in his mind that he doesn't even attempt to do a certain very easy thing. *It is a serious mistake to masquerade "I don't want to" for "I can't."* You may be right in saying the former, but wrong in insisting on the latter. A similar situation occurs with fear. We repeat day after day, "I'm afraid, I'm afraid," and finally we completely shy away from the particular situation that causes fear. Thus the fear becomes embedded in both our bodies and our minds.

It is therefore advisable that you build new and improved responses by repetition of "I can do it, I am courageous, I'll be all right." Repeating these new and better thoughts again and again will help overcome the feeling of fear. This is much healthier than trying to cover up or forget the old fearful ideas. The time and energy required to combat or bury old ideas can be far more effectively utilized to create new ones.

HINTS FOR SUCCESSFUL APPLICATION

Create an appealing picture of yourself as being happy, healthy, and useful (or any other grouping of your main desires and values). This assurance is not boastfulness; it is merely internal certainty that *life offers no challenges beyond your capacity.* And note, apropos of this picture of yourself, that suggestions received from other people have no effect on you unless you yourself act upon them. In the long run, therefore, *all suggestion is autosuggestion.*

The best results from constant autosuggestion are obtained while we are in a state of thorough relaxation, when the mental "censor" is off guard. Then our thoughts can find their way without hindrance into the subconscious mind.

Make use of habit. Our habits of thought or action, when not interfered with, perpetuate themselves because they simplify our ordinary activities enormously. Habit not only digs a groove but waxes and shines the surface so that we slide along it with the greatest ease. So, as soon as you establish healthful or useful habits, see to it that these shallow paths become well-worn highways. With every repetitive act, your personality becomes just so much stronger. Therefore, it is vital to establish the habit of having faith and confidence in yourself.

This process may profitably be employed in the morning when you get up, at mealtimes, during waiting periods or rest pauses, at night when you go to sleep, and at every other convenient opportunity. The key words or phrases should be repeated consciously and determinedly—loud enough for you to hear, and yet quietly so no one else can hear them! If we hold these beneficial thoughts at "peaceful" times, when we are relaxed in our bodies and quiet in our minds, they will gradually take root and stay with us, and become a part of our natures.

Remember that you cannot relax if you constantly suggest to yourself such tension builders as fear, hate, and failure. If you *think* of yourself as unworthy and incapable and persist in *acting* that way, you are in danger of *becoming* both helpless and hopeless. If, however, you recognize your possibilities, you can revive your dormant inner powers. For instance, if you constantly suggest to yourself such thoughts as, "I *can* do this job; I *am* fit for it; I *have* the strength," the ideas starting as abstract symbolism become anchored in your mind, and you can then act them out concretely. The important thing is never to lose awareness of your untapped ability.

10.

For Minor Stresses

WHAT CAN YOU DO ABOUT YOUR FEARS?
WHY GET ANGRY? · WORRY ONLY WHEN RELAXED!
ARE YOU EVER IRRITATED? · ILLNESS AND RELAXATION
HOW TO CARE EMOTIONALLY FOR THE SICK
IS THERE DISCORD IN YOUR FAMILY?
ARE YOUR DECISIONS JUST?
HOW TO CONTROL EXCESSIVE ELATION
HOW TO OUTWIT MOODS OF DEPRESSION
FIVE WAYS TO COMBAT DEPRESSION

Do you make mountains out of molehills? Most people do at one time or another! Yet to meet slight provocations there is no need for a quickened tempo, a "flying off the handle." Nor is there need to continue in the same rhythm of intense excitement long after the *cause* that aroused that emotion has gone away. In other words, don't *shout* when the situation calls for a *whisper,* or *rush* when *slow motion* is implied.

When we are relaxed, we can be more calm and deliberate in our thinking. We do not exaggerate our hurt feelings, and we are better able to find the wisest solution in dealing with our disturbed emotions, without hurting ourselves or anyone else.

WHAT CAN YOU DO ABOUT YOUR FEARS?

The strongest and most disabling emotion that we have to deal with is fear. Not the fear that springs from an awareness of actual physical peril: we face it instinctively by running or fighting. It is the pathological state of fear against which we need to be on guard—the fear that evokes panic long before the actual danger appears and lurks in us long after the episode is past. This is a subconscious fear—a memory of former threats of danger, which perpetuated itself as an emotional scar. To be fearful in the sight of real danger is normal and understandable, but to be panicky in a crisis which has no genuine basis of danger is not only unproductive, but frequently leads to acts that are either senseless or cruel.

With fear comes tension. As soon as we grasp the significance of this associated fact, we realize that this evil combination can be attacked on either flank. *If we reduce the tension we lessen the fear.* And if the fear is lessened, our muscles become relaxed. With the decrease of tension comes clarity of vision and a ripening of our senses. New plans become possible; new ideas come to the surface.

A short period of complete relaxation of body as well as mind will give you a *fresh perspective.* By saying to yourself, "During this period of rest I will not permit my fears to dominate me. I will be quiet; I will be at ease; later I will again cope with the sources of my fears; but for the time being, I must simply hold them in check"; you should be better able to break the vicious cycle.

When the session is over, your fears no longer will seem to be quite so unsurmountable. Then too, whatever decisions you reach *after* a period of relaxation tend to be more mature and of a nature you are less likely to regret.

WHY GET ANGRY?

Like fear, anger has an adverse effect upon our entire being. A blazing attack of anger can temporarily derange the functioning of our whole body. It evokes muscle tension, nerve irritability, changes in blood circulation, and heart action, and may impair the digestion. The severity of the tension produced depends upon how deeply or how long we have been under emotional strain.

The immediate release of anger is the *explosive* performance of the child, the immature adult, or the psychopath. The wise individual allows his anger pressure to escape steadily and easily. A short period of waiting—the proverbially simple but neglected "count ten"—helps. The greater the anger, the more we should multiply "count ten" —preferably while sitting or lying down. Then start to count slowly . . . *very* slowly. When you become mentally and physically relaxed, you are better able to assess your anger.

Anger cannot be wished away. Nor can it be easily suppressed or ignored. It liberates energy which must be harnessed and then discharged harmlessly. We can better cope with it when we understand its source.

Ask yourself what was the real cause of your emotional upheaval. Most frequently we become angry because our self-esteem is low, or we are expecting too much from ourselves or others. Many frictions that develop—of a domestic, social, or business nature—could be better coped with if we had a greater appreciation of ourselves. When we think of ourselves as being worthy and strong, and look upon provocations as a challenge to self-improvement or as errors to avoid, we take frustrations and impediments in our stride.

When our ego is hurt, we may think we have a legitimate excuse to become angry. But generally speaking, "getting even" is not an appropriate way of releasing this vital emotional energy. Deep hurts require deep thoughts to overcome them. Usually *second* thoughts are best.

WORRY ONLY WHEN RELAXED!

An old man was asked, "How is it that you look so young and happy?" He replied, "When I work, I work; and when I worry, I sleep." Next to sleeping, effortless relaxation is best.

When worry overtakes you, give yourself time to think out your problem and its solution. This can be accomplished best when your muscles are relaxed and your brain is clear.

Sometimes worry comes from taking too seriously the adage, "I am the master of my fate." Such worry arises from feeling that only the "I" at this moment must make the decision, that "I" am alone, that the "I" is all-important. This exaggeration of the Self is not so much vanity as forgetfulness of one's relationship to the larger order of the Universe. *Sometimes worry can be overcome just by making a decision one way or the other, rather than stewing in prolonged indecision.*

ARE YOU EVER IRRITATED?

To meet irritation with limpness may seem strange but usually it is effective because reaction to the irritant is always much less when our muscles are not tense and tightened in preparation for an uncomfortable situation. When we become tense in the face of the struggle against the expected irritant, we are half exhausted to begin with. The opening of the battle finds us with much of our energy already depleted. For instance, in a physical fall, skilled tumblers or sportsmen know that the easiest way to fall with the least amount of harm is just to make yourself limp and "let yourself go"; very seldom do such athletes have wounds or fractures. Similarly, in a dentist's chair, those who have learned to *yield* to pain or "go along with it" find that the pain is not as excruciating as when the whole nervous system becomes irritated, the body rigid and full of fear—for then the pain is exaggerated.

This concept by no means negates the reality of illness, pain, fear, anger, frustration, etc. It means that we do recognize those sensations and emotions clearly, but we are always aware of the *inner strength within us to overcome them.* We need not be hurt deeply or lastingly by our experiences.

ILLNESS AND RELAXATION

When ill, we need to practice implicitly all the standard rules of relaxation. For instance, an appropriate way to deal with digestive disturbances, in addition to following a doctor's orders, is to relax for a while *before* meals, particularly the evening meal. This is helpful to digestion for the simple reason that, at the end of your working day, your energy is below par, and your nerves are undoubtedly taut, because of the normal tension of work and travel.

When you come home tired and hungry at the same time, it is better to relax at least for a few minutes. Your "hunger pains" can easily be quieted down by drinking a glass of water or clear broth. When your body is rested, you will then digest and enjoy your food better.

Seeing how relaxation helps to relieve minor distress, it should be obvious that to some extent it can be beneficial for serious ills. Illness or pain can be aggravated easily and needlessly by the heightened nervous strain which springs from anxiety or fear, also by the superabundant sympathy given to us by misguided friends and relatives. Learning to accept or to tolerate our pain helps us to bear it until we can be relieved of it.

HOW TO CARE EMOTIONALLY FOR THE SICK

When you are caring for someone who is sick in your home, you yourself need to relax. For how can you be efficient when your muscles are taut, your nerves on edge, and your mind full of fears and worries? But if your body is free from tension, it is easier for you to assume the attitude of the skilled nurse who takes the patient's irritability, pain, and suffering in her stride. You may even succeed in having a faint smile on your face and in your heart. With frequent short intervals of relaxation, you will be surprised how tolerant you become of the patient's irritability.

When you leave someone else in charge of the sickroom throw your burdens completely off your shoulders. If you allow worries to follow you, then no matter how much you relax physically, you will not be able to chase away mental and emotional fatigue. By thus bearing a needless load, you will return to your charge nervous and tense, thus making yourself therapeutically useless to the patient, as well as undermining your own health. Remember that *your responsibility has ceased when you are doing your very best, even if that best falls short of meeting all that the situation requires.* In other words, learn to relax away your worries if you would be a good nurse.

IS THERE DISCORD IN YOUR FAMILY?

When there is discord in the home, the ability to relax can be mighty useful. Do not let yourself become involved painfully. When other people are disagreeing or arguing, and you see the solution, or think of a helpful suggestion, hold it back for a while. Stay on the sidelines by relaxing or meditating in another room for a few minutes. By doing this you give yourself an opportunity to gather and check your thoughts, and crystallize your ideas in more concrete form. At the same time, your argumentative relatives have had a chance to talk themselves out and to quiet down a bit. You are then in the position of the referee, who, while the fight goes on, does not jump in the middle to be hit by the participants. But at *the end* of the emotional or intellectual family bout, if your opinion is asked, it will make a much more lasting impression.

Again, when you find yourself in an argument with someone, give your "antagonist" an opportunity to talk himself out. When he has finished shouting, a temporary vacuum has been created in his mind which you can then fill by having your say in a controlled, calm, and friendly voice. You may also ask yourself questions such as, "Is it possible that he or she is all wrong and only I am right, or vice versa?" "Anyway, what's all the shouting about?" "Must I have the last word?"

During your silent period, you also captured valuable time in which to collect your wits, to quiet your tone of voice, and to assume an attitude to fit the specific occasion.

ARE YOUR DECISIONS JUST?

Never be hasty in solving problems or situations of great consequence. The real emergencies of life are so rare that the time-honored rules of conduct, such as "think before you speak," or "count ten," especially while relaxed, can almost invariably be used. And *unless* a dire emergency exists, your lack of haste will always give you satisfaction and make things easier for other people.

Major decisions should be made only when, to the best of our knowledge and insight, the final choice appears to be for the greatest good of everyone involved, and not just for ourselves. Such decisions cannot be figured out in haste, at the moment when the need for them arises. We have to give ourselves time to think things over. But before that period of thinking must come a period of body ease, and mind ease—relaxation.

HOW TO CONTROL EXCESSIVE ELATION

Exuberance—agreeable excitement—is a wonderful feeling. It is the zest of living. But it needs to be controlled; else it will lead to exhaustion, loss of emotional control and, finally, to depression.

Start harnessing your excess exuberance by slow stretching exercises in the lying position. Elation produces strong, "unregulated" breathing. Therefore, concentrate on making your breathing deeper and more regularly rhythmic. Anchor the word "quiet" in your mind. Keep on repeating it *subvocally*. Soon you succeed in reducing that bubbling energy of elation which can spill wastefully all over your nerves. Control of the *peaks* is indispensable to a mastery of the *depths* with which they are commonly associated.

HOW TO OUTWIT MOODS OF DEPRESSION

Depression of spirits and bodily inactivity go hand in glove. When depressed, we are usually in a state of *slump*. One may therefore ask, "Isn't this what takes place during the state of relaxation?" Actually, just the reverse is true. During the state of depression, the entire muscular frame is taut. Self-pity causes glandular imbalance and a certain stagnation of circulation; digestion and elimination are faulty.

When the human being is gravely distressed, his head is tilted forward and down, the chest is sunk, the breathing shallow; the bend of the back and the swing of the limbs show he's in a stooped position. *The deeper his depression, the worse his posture.* This is noticeable in many "nervous" people. They develop the slouching gait, and worst of all, even become unaware of it.

When depressed, morose, and despondent, be *persistent* in practicing relaxation. Breathe deeply. Even if you don't feel like it, stretch and yawn your blues away. As you persevere you gain better nerve control, and *your outlook on life* brightens correspondingly. Soon you notice your muscular tautness beginning to leave you. Your breathing becomes fuller and freer. Circulation quickens of its own accord. All your bodily functions normalize themselves. Vital energy is more in evidence. Of course, proper posture and ideomotor exercise are only *two* of the several basic requirements for full mental and physical well-being, so don't assume that these factors alone will do everything you wish.

FIVE WAYS TO COMBAT DEPRESSION

1. Your attitude to inner or spontaneously aroused depression needs to be the same as your attitude to inclement weather. When you find yourself in this depressed state, wait until it's over, saying, "There's nothing I can do about it. I can take it. I will not allow my soul to be soaked through by it. I will protect myself through inner calm and wait confidently until it's over."

2. You can muster your reserves of inner strength and determine to go on in spite of everything. You will not permit the encircling gloom to stop you from doing what you have to do. Defy it, and go on anyway. "If I can't run, I'll walk, creep, or crawl." At all costs keep alive the spirit of forward movement.

3. Attempt to work off, walk off, or talk off your depression. The important thing is to keep busy and to *do something* rather than to stew in your own juice.

4. You can sometimes obtain good results by writing out the various reasons which you think caused your depression. This may clarify your thoughts and thus lighten your mental burden.

5. If you are temporarily unable to do anything about your unfavorable situation, relax fully to its presence in your life. Your blues—or "browns"—take on a lighter and brighter hue as you ease your face and eyes, stretch your large muscles, quiet your inner thoughts, and start rhythmic breathing. Then stay put until you gradually pull yourself out of your depression.

11.

How to Sleep

TWELVE STEPS TO WOO SLEEP
SLEEPING ARRANGEMENTS
A WARM BATH · THE RIGHT POSITION
OLD STAND-BYS · THE HELPFUL SHEEP
SLEEPING IS LIKE MEMORY · UNWIND
CATALOGUE YOUR THOUGHTS
THE WORD "QUIET" · MUSIC TO SLEEP BY
A GENEROUS ATTITUDE
CONSOLIDATED GLADNESS

SLEEPLESSNESS, when it is not a result of disease, is usually a carry-over of the stress and anxiety of civilized living. There may be many reasons for your restlessness. Here are some, but not all of them:

Although this fact is usually not recognized, bright color affects our sleep. For ages the human eye has been accustomed to sleeping in utter darkness. Thus bedroom colors should be a soothing blue, green, or gray.

When soundproofing is not possible or too expensive, the only measure that the city dweller can take to lessen noise is to drape the bedroom windows heavily, and place woolen rugs on the floor.

Excess mental or physical activity during the day, and especially shortly before retiring, may keep you "keyed-up," tense, and overstimulated. *Intense experiences noticeably heighten or depress the emotions.*

Avoid eating indigestible meals before retiring. If it is possible for you to eat your heavy meal at noon and your light meal in the evening, you may find that your digestive processes will be completed by bedtime and your sleep more restful. Constipation is a frequent source of sleeplessness with some people.

Eliminate resentment in your mind against those who fall asleep quickly and effortlessly. Banish thoughts such as "I must sleep," "Others are sleeping; why can't I?" "It's late," "I have to get up early." Such thoughts are definite sleep-chasers.

If you have established the habit of going to sleep at a given time, avoid rushing yourself to meet that schedule. This will defeat your very purpose. When you overemphasize the importance of always preparing yourself for bed thus and so, if for some reason or other your self-imposed conditions cannot be met, you will have difficulty in falling asleep. Any procedure which has a tendency to become a fixed "must" should be avoided.

Another common cause of insomnia is sleeping in a strange bed, or going to bed too early or too late. This will disturb you until you become accustomed to these different conditions.

Test yourself to see if your sleeping would be more restful if you changed your mattress. If it is unusually soft, change to one which gives you more support. Very hard mattresses are usually not conducive to sleep. Much depends upon your body contour and your sleeping habits.

Check to see if your room is well-ventilated and neither

too warm nor too cold. Often insomnia is due to some hidden or remote nerve irritations.

Is your mind full of thoughts about some *unfinished schedule of commitments?* Relieve yourself of those thoughts as you undress, by the inner command of "quiet." Do you fall asleep in a state of physical exhaustion, full of fears, worries, hates, regrets, or guilt? Then you are bound to get up in the morning irritable and fatigued.

There are many other reasons, known only to yourself, why your sleep is restless or insufficient. Sleeplessness is commonly overcome as soon as its causes are removed.

The amount of sleep that you should have depends upon many factors, such as: your age, physique, mental or physical activity, nervous temperament, and whether you take short rest periods during the day. Your intuitive sense is usually the best guide; for most adults eight hours in bed is ample.

Occasional sleeplessness should hold no terror. The sleep you lose one night, you readily make up in the next night or two. Become attuned to and rely upon your rhythmostat. It regulates the amount of sleep you need, just as it regulates the amount of oxygen you need. But if you habitually lose too much sleep, your health will be impaired. However, before resorting to sleeping pills, try every conceivable rational and natural step.

By adhering to one or more of the following rules, sleep should come to you more easily than it has heretofore.

TWELVE STEPS TO WOO SLEEP

1. Sleeping arrangements

These should be as free from discomfort as possible. Your *blankets should not be too heavy*. You can obtain additional warmth when necessary by placing a woolen blanket beneath your sheet. Night clothes must have no annoying features. Some people find it a great comfort to sleep in the nude. Emancipate yourself from awkward ways of falling asleep. Make sure that your mind is free from emotions and that your body is completely relaxed. If your sleeping habits are annoying to your mate (or vice versa!), "Sleep alone and like it."

2. THE WARM BATH

A warm bath is usually conducive to sleep. But be sure not to rub yourself vigorously with a towel after the bath, because that stimulates the nerve ends and may make you wide awake. Dry yourself by patting the towel against your body. This is soothing, like the mother's gentle pat which calms her baby.

3. THE RIGHT POSITION

Place yourself in the most comfortable position, whether on your back, the front of your body, or your side, whichever is most convenient for you. If you like to sleep on your side, don't hinder your breathing by wrapping your arms around your chest. Place the free arm at the side of your body so that your breathing will be easier.

Place your pillow so as to take up the space between your shoulder and head (see illustration). Then your head assumes the same correct position as though you were sitting or standing. When you roll over on your other side, and are dimly aware of doing so, again adjust the pillow in the same position. Soon habit sets in and you will adjust your pillow unconsciously.

When you are about to fall asleep, and you have assumed a comfortable position, remain in the same position in spite of little annoyances. Constant conscious shifting (as distinct from those reflex adjustments of which the sleeper remains unaware) is a hindrance to repose.

Some authorities do not advise sleeping on the back. For one reason, it is bound to cause snoring. If you lie on your

back and do not snore, your teeth will usually be tight together and your vocal cords become tense. If, however, you habitually sleep on your back, see that the pillow is a small one; this will prevent your head from pressing against your chest. If you like your head to be elevated, place an additional pillow under the head of the mattress (see page 24).

4. OLD STAND-BYS

When you are still awake after a half hour or so, read some uninteresting book, such as a dictionary (unless you happen to be a lexicographer!), write that long-delayed letter, listen to the radio, have a very light midnight snack, or take a warm, nonstimulating drink. (The old-fashioned idea of drinking warm milk before bedtime now has the backing of the best scientific psychologists.) Then go to bed again with the indifferent attitude of "I don't care a hoot whether I fall asleep now or later."

5. THE HELPFUL SHEEP

Our health is seldom impaired by the occasional loss of a couple of hours' sleep. When it does not come readily, try the old-fashioned custom of counting sheep. As they jump over your bed, take a good look at them; watch their facial expressions; give each of them a name. If this doesn't bring the desired results, walking about in the room or in the fresh air may be helpful.

There is a nice story about an old farmer who tried to put himself to sleep by counting sheep. Finally in the middle of the night he called his doctor and said, "I still can't sleep. I see all my sheep jumping over my fence and into the next pasture." The farmer was advised to go out and investigate. When he did, he found his sheep fast asleep. He saw the beautiful midnight sky, studded with thousands of stars, and as he stood on the hilltop, he drank in the beauty of the peaceful stillness of the night. He was refreshed by the cool air, and became delightfully tired from his walk. Upon his return, he, too, fell fast asleep!

The moral of this story is: If you can't sleep, go out for a walk, or sit by the window. Don't make a jail out of your bed; you don't have to stay in it. You are a free American!

6. SLEEPING IS LIKE MEMORY

We cannot force ourselves to fall asleep any more than we can force ourselves to remember. When a thought, name, or number does not come readily to our minds, we find it extremely difficult to recall it intentionally. Often, when we stop trying, it comes back to us. The same principle applies to sleep. When we lie down with the express and eager purpose of falling asleep, we usually become irritated if unconsciousness does not come swiftly enough. If, however, we lie quietly with our entire body and mind at rest, sleep will most likely come of its own accord.

7. UNWIND

If you're "all wound up" from a day of extraordinary physical or mental activity, stop fighting your pillows. Instead, release your tension of the day by gentle slow exercise, stretching and yawning and slow, deep, rhythmic breathing. You will sleep better and awaken more refreshed if you spend a transitional period of ten minutes practicing relaxation in preparation for sleep. *The method of relaxation already recommended here is an unrivaled aid to restful slumber.* By practicing it, you may fall asleep so quickly that no other steps will be necessary.

8. CATALOGUE YOUR THOUGHTS

Check over whatever thoughts or worries may still be on your mind. Then first, dismiss the past as something beyond your power to recapture. Second, leave to destiny all problems having to do with the remote future. Third, jot down notes about the unfinished business of the day so as to clear your mind of all immediate problems. This is the famous Osler principle of living only twenty-four hours at a time. If on the very verge of sleep, you should feel you have forgotten something of real importance, and cannot be sure that you will remember it the next day, make a note of it on a pad which should be placed handy to your bed. You will sleep more peacefully once you have done this.

9. THE WORD "QUIET"

This word, which we have already mentioned, possesses a beneficial signal value for insomnia. The use of the admonishing word "quiet" helps to slow down all mental and physical processes. The word "sleep" may also have a partial hypnotic effort on some people. However, students of insomnia know that when a person who is attempting to fall asleep uses the well-known formula of "sleep, sleep," he may become angry and resentful when slumber does not follow within what he considers a reasonable time. He will concentrate so wholeheartedly on it that if he cannot get to sleep, his disgust with his failure will keep him even more awake.

By contrast, the word "quiet" means only that you are giving yourself the suggestion that you are at peace with the world. You are in a sense *indifferent* as to when sleep may come; your aim is merely to quiet your thoughts. Therefore, by quieting your mind and body *before* going to bed, your sleep is bound to be deeper and more restful. And, of course, the more soundly and uninterruptedly you sleep, the more rested you will be when you awaken.

10. MUSIC TO SLEEP BY

Some authorities claim that music, unless presented discriminatingly, may be an impediment to sound sleep. For many of the associations it evokes are exciting rather than calming. But if your mind is in a turmoil, the greater background sound of soothing music may distract you from your inner stress. So under such conditions, soothing music may be helpful in putting you to sleep.

Of course the same music which lulled you may later wake you up. But by that time, your disturbing thoughts have been dissipated. And now you can turn off the music, and roll over for peaceful slumber.

11. A GENEROUS ATTITUDE

An important step in restful sleep, as well as in relaxation, is to learn to *be generous* toward yourself and other people as well. Resentment against your poor sleeping habits, anxiety, anger, or fear will upset your mental equilibrium. Conversely, gracious, generous, and loving thoughts create not only a serenity and calmness in your mind, but also relaxation in your body. Such thoughts have a way of becoming automatic and habitual.

12. CONSOLIDATED GLADNESS

When on the verge of falling asleep, does your mind turn to the unhappy events of your past, or to anxieties about the future? Do you weave them into a heavy, wet blanket of gloom, which bears down upon you and smothers you? If sleep doesn't come readily, direct your thoughts to relatively happy aspects of your life. Obliterate further all unpleasant thoughts. Consolidate into pleasant memories all the *joys* you have had. They are a quieting approach to sleep.

12.

Understand Your Attitudes

TELL YOUR STORY
FIND YOURSELF WITH PEN AND INK
WHY DID YOU DO IT? · EARLY INFLUENCES
EMOTION AND INTELLIGENCE
FOR GREATER SELF-UNDERSTANDING
ASSETS AND LIABILITIES
ADVANTAGES OF SELF-UNDERSTANDING

RELAXATION cannot be achieved merely through physical ease. Self-understanding is also a necessity. By searching out your basic attitudes, you will not only appreciate your strengths; you will also recognize your weaknesses, and discover how to overcome them. As *you* are the most important person with whom you will ever have to deal, no other task can be more fascinating and profitable to you nor more beneficial to your total welfare.

Self-understanding depends not upon the number or even the excellence of the books you read, but upon how much thought you give to applying earnestly any newly gained knowledge. Your former experiences can also give you added knowledge in understanding yourself, for inherently, this task can be done only by the person primarily concerned; in other words, by *you!*

Of course, expert aid is necessary and useful when your load is heavy. But recognize the fact that there is a great shortage of mental experts; and besides, a complete analysis requires a great deal of money and time. Thus many have discovered that considerable self-understanding can be gained by their own efforts. We can, with diligence and patience, discover the reasons for most of our tenseness, irritability, restlessness, or frustrations. The following are some of the most common causes of unhappiness.

1. Conflicting inner thoughts and antagonistic reactions to life's situations.
2. Failure to understand one's purpose in life.
3. Uncertainty concerning major and minor life values.
4. Disappointment with oneself.
5. Inappropriate attitudes toward self and others.
6. Inability to differentiate between the hereditary influences which cannot be altered and those traits, habits, thoughts, and environmental influences that can be changed.

These, as well as many other conditions of stress, lead to nerve-muscle tensions, which tie you almost literally into physical and mental knots, heightening your mental confusion until all your real problems become greatly exaggerated.

But as you progress in self-knowledge and mature emotionally you will realize that, just as your healthy body has sufficient inner wisdom to carry on all its amazing physical and chemical functions, so your mind, when calm, has enough inherent wisdom to find solutions for your everyday problems.

Now, before going further, it is only fair to warn you that, when you discover your personality faults, you may be momentarily frightened or upset; but remember that your unrecognized faults can be an even greater source of irritation. Self-knowledge can increase your emotional will to change, heighten your self-reliance, and give you a more mature attitude toward yourself and others.

There are at least two helpful techniques that you may use in exploring your thoughts.

TELL YOUR STORY

If you are blessed with a wise and understanding friend to whom you can talk your heart out, you may get not only emotional relief but fresh insight into your difficulties. But guard yourself against the sad possibility that, in the process of unburdening yourself, you may lose that friend. Not many people want to hear a long story of gloom. Therefore, make your troubles interesting. Put some drama and humor into the telling. Prevent yourself at all costs from becoming a bore. Stop often for a breather. If your friend's interest lags, change the subject, or better yet, give him a chance to tell you about his own distressing experiences.

It is remarkable what relief we sometimes gain by telling our troubles to a sympathetic listener.

FIND YOURSELF WITH PEN AND INK

But a better way to gain self-understanding, and one that has more far-reaching value, is to start writing something about your life story. Many psychologists recommend a half hour of daily writing until the job is done. When too much disturbing emotional material wells up at one time, do not feel that you have to write it all out at that moment. It is bound to come back to you later on.

Now and then you may write about how badly you were treated as a child or by fate. But at such times you should search your memory for those occasions when you were cared for with love and understanding. If such pleasant early recollections do not come readily to mind, write about your more recent pleasant experiences and think of the nice people you know or remember.

Likewise when you write poignantly about your loneliness, reflect also upon the beneficial uses to which solitude can be put. If you recall your experiences with former poverty, rejoice in your comparative comfort at the present time. In this manner, you will "sugar-coat" your unhappy memories.

Grammar, style, coherence, the language you use, do not matter. Neither is it necessary to question whether or not your thoughts are reasonable, sensible, practical, or obscene. Nor should you ask yourself, "What good will it do me?" You are simply baring your soul to yourself. Remember that whatever you write is for your eyes alone; keep it under lock and key. After rereading it, you may destroy it. Or if you decide to consult a counselor who merits your full confidence, you may unhesitatingly show him your material and shorten the time required for a complete analysis.

Do not hurry with your task. No one is rushing you. Your success will depend upon expressing your thoughts and feelings freely and fully. Bringing them up from your subconscious tends to give you greater peace of mind. This alone is sufficient reason for adopting the procedure.

As you write about some of your earliest experiences, tears may come too, especially if you are sentimentally inclined. But at least such tears are more productive than sheer crying without writing. For now your grief is a matter of record. When you think of the same hurt again, you can say to yourself, "Well, anyway, it's all on paper." Then reread what you have written and study it for its implications. This procedure is bound to help you more than to keep distressing experiences locked up in your mind, because the turmoil you have felt, which has been like some subterranean storm going around and around in your mind, finally escapes and is transformed via pen and ink.

So during your self-search, do not expect to be especially happy. Your attempt to understand yourself may be compared to the long-postponed renovation of a house when we finally decide that neglected repairs or improvements are necessary. Having lived in the house for a long time, we are quite comfortable, and easily overlook the inconveniences. But what a pleasure it is when the improvements have finally been made. Similarly with the remodeling that comes from self-understanding. Although you should not expect to do a complete or artistic job, yet every small gain in knowledge about yourself can be turned into a fresh source of strength.

WHY DID YOU DO IT?

You will find the habit of self-analysis by pen and paper helpful in many ways. For instance, how many times have we said to ourselves, "Why in the world did I do or say that?" when we have unintentionally hurt someone else or done something particularly stupid. If you hesitate in giving a *self*-satisfactory reason, the delay is a fair indication that you are not fully aware of some of the motives that prompted your behavior.

Try writing down whatever thoughts come into your mind regarding *why* you said or did the puzzling thing. Put on paper an account of your questionable behavior and beside this what you actually wanted to do or say but didn't. What was your real intention? Write down what you attempted to *hide* by your behavior; or state your doubts about it. Upon rereading these comments, you may be able to better evaluate the entire episode, thereby taking an important step in the direction of self-improvement.

EARLY INFLUENCES

Your writings may show you that some of your current troubles are the result of ideas impressed upon you when you were a child—such ideas as, "You're very smart," "You're very stupid," "You're wonderful," or "You'll never amount to anything." Your early admirers or tormentors may have been one hundred per cent right when they complimented or berated you. But you have since grown up. Experience should have proved to you that you are not the "dumbhead" that you may or may not have been as a child, and on the other hand you should not expect all the good things of life to be served to you on a silver platter.

If you experienced strong frustration and rejection in your childhood, why should you be angry with yourself if you cannot now express your love freely? For after all, the power of giving and receiving affection was deadened in you at the very source in early life. Thus you may now find it difficult to blossom suddenly into a loving personality.

Conversely, can you blame yourself for having an exaggerated need for friendship and love if you were excessively loved and overprotected in your early years? You should not expect such demonstrative care, now that you are an adult, especially if you are living in close contact with a repressed individual such as the person described in the paragraph above.

If in your formative period you were not allowed much initiative or offered much encouragement to grow emotionally and to do things for others, don't condemn yourself unduly when you awaken to the fact that you are still selfish and immature. Contrariwise, if you were a "beast of burden" in childhood, this may explain your present inability to take it easy.

These examples of early influences should help you to understand your present behavior. Once aware of them, there is no reason for you to despair. When you discover that you are in *some* ways emotionally immature, do not feel too troubled. Practically everyone is immature in some respects. Slight mental quirks and minor errors of behavior are part of everyone's standard equipment. Becoming aware of these character defects is always a healthy step in the direction of correcting them. You would not allow a "spoiled" child to rule a community of adults, so why should you permit childish thoughts to rule you?

EMOTION AND INTELLIGENCE

In making a pen-and-ink study of yourself you may find the following charts for self-analysis helpful. To determine whether you are ruled chiefly by emotions or mature intelligence ask yourself whether you are habitually dominated by your uncontrolled feelings or whether you needlessly repress your feelings and impulses of self-expression. If you swing to either extreme, you subject yourself to much unnecessary unhappiness as well as loss of self-esteem.

Rate yourself on a scale from 1 to 10 on each question:

1. Before starting a plan or project, I always have in my mind a clear picture of its purpose and the goal that I wish to reach. _____

2. I always attempt, to the best of my ability, to find the motives behind my acts. _____

3. Truth and verified knowledge are always more precious to me than my particular opinions or cherished beliefs. _____

4. When proved wrong in any argument, I do not fight back with ridicule or sarcasm, or make a personal issue out of it. _____

5. The tendency is strong within me not to fall "hook, line, and sinker" for whatever I may happen to hear, read, or see. I try to evaluate every assertion from several angles. _____

6. When thinking through a problem, I constantly endeavor to be accurate in my thinking, taking into consideration such factors as "who, when, how, where, what, and why." _____

7. When I once set a goal for myself, and feel that it is good and necessary, I do not permit anyone to dissuade me from it. _____

8. I am always willing to change my opinion in the face of new and pertinent evidence. _____

9. I do not yield to anyone on really vital matters, but on minor trivial matters, I readily yield to the wishes of others. _____

10. Whenever possible, I try not to dominate others, and don't permit others to dominate me. _____

11. I recognize clearly that my age is not a barrier to improvement. _____

12. I recognize that age, sex, race, creed, etc., are in themselves an insufficient basis for respect. _____

13. I know the difference between helping others and dominating them. _____

14. I realize and accept the fact that I am important largely to myself alone, and by the very nature of things, my feelings, troubles, and opinions are of little concern to most others. _____

15. I attempt to avoid self-pity, and know that only by being socially useful, and making other people happy, can I find happiness. _____

If your total is close to 150, you probably have too high an opinion of yourself. If you feel very inferior and tend to devaluate yourself, your percentage will be very low— around 50. One hundred points would be a pretty good average for the well-balanced individual.

FOR GREATER SELF-UNDERSTANDING

Of course, the reader should understand that the questions which follow merely exemplify hundreds of related queries that might be incorporated into a complete personality questionnaire. In general, it may be said that you should first ascertain through earnest self-questioning what you personally believe you require to achieve the greatest degree of contentment and happiness. By writing, you make in effect a blueprint of action. Patiently, and with faith in your heart, give yourself honest answers to the following:

How well do I know my *real* self?

Do I *expect* too much of myself or others?

Why am I dissatisfied with my present behavior?

Am I living up to my "image" of myself?

What deeds and situations would give me the most contentment or happiness?

What *inner* annoyances am I cognizant of?

Am I *sufficiently considerate* of the next one's wishes or needs?

Is my behavior normally satisfactory to others?

Do I understand why people act the way they do toward me?

Should I anticipate many sudden changes in myself?

Have I the tendency to seek excess dependence or independence?

Is the need for the approval of my group so strong in me that I dare not assert myself?

Why is the lust to dominance such a powerful force in me, and for what purpose am I using it?

Why am I such a harsh critic of myself?

Or why am I so lenient with myself and critical of others?

Why am I so timid with respect to one person, and so brave in regard to another?

Why do I do things which I shouldn't do, and not do things which I should?

Do I think others are perfect?

Why should I hate one certain person and like another?

Why do I react to recurring situations as I do?

You should not become upset if you fail to find immediate solutions to your problems. The answer to any troubling question seldom comes just when you are most intensely seeking it. Later, when you think of something else, or after a restful night's sleep, even during your sleep, the solution may suddenly reveal itself. Many times you may wake up in the morning after having given much previous study and thought to a certain problem, and find that the solution is clear to you.

Self-understanding should lead to a more intelligent organization of your motives. Merely gaining the knowledge is not enough unless it results in a better life plan.

ASSETS AND LIABILITIES

Honesty is the obvious basis for an accurate self-appraisal, because self-deceit is usually lurking in your mind. There is always the possibility that your feelings of self-esteem, self-justification, self-sufficiency, or any other emotional habit pattern may distort the truth when it comes to your consciousness. A constant rechecking of your conclusions helps. Second thoughts are usually clearer and nearer to the truth. To reassess your personality, list your assets on one side of the page, and your liabilities on the other, as shown below. Of course, one character trait doesn't necessarily balance another. But to know oneself better, an inventory of such assets and liabilities in conduct becomes a *must*.

Assets of Mr. X	Liabilities of Mr. X
1. Earnestness	Lack of scholarly preparation
2. Ability to undergo hardships	Poor physical resources
3. Desire for success	Feeling of inadequacy
4. Willingness to forego pleasures	Strong primitive drives
5. Altruistic motives	Search for security
6. Perseverance	Impatience
7. Received satisfactory academic grades	Did some cheating in school
8. Control of temper	Sense of frustration due to inhibiting emotional expression
9. Ability to complete studies and hold jobs	Requires forceful effort to complete a task
10. Possession of a fair amount of self-esteem	Often overcome by inner self-inadequacy
11. Ability to *make* friends	Unable to *keep* friends
12. Easily obtains the confidence of others	Conscious of self-abasement
13. Gained community respect	Is known as a "yes man"
14. Easily forgives hurts inflicted by others	Tendency to develop a martyr attitude

Inventories of this sort for general self-assessment can be greatly extended depending on how much the above "ready-made" list of terms means to you. *Make up an in-*

dependent inventory of your own particular "traits on hand." You will thus have a more realistic catalogue of whatever mental and emotional equipment you already possess, the major liabilities you have to subdue, and the chief assets you should strive to develop.

Often what you assume to be a personality asset may in fact be a liability, and vice versa. If you wear yourself out in your attempt to do everything perfectly, you may consider this to be an asset; but if such behavior leaves you in a state of tension, then it is a liability. On the other hand, your feeling of inadequacy, which you consider to be a liability, is actually an asset, if it will give you the necessary drive for self-improvement.

ADVANTAGES OF SELF-UNDERSTANDING

What else can you expect from a search for self-understanding in addition to a blueprint for your improvement?

It will help you see that your personality is influenced by many factors, so you will be less tempted to blame any particular person, event, or even yourself for your present situation.

It may remove some of the common but unnecessary guilt feelings that are a hang-over from your childhood.

It can make you realize that none of us stands alone; that our major problems of living are astonishingly similar; and that even the solutions fall into easily recognizable patterns.

It may lead to greater emotional security and contentment.

It will make you a more relaxed personality, because your tensions decrease of their own accord as you discover the reasons for your behavior.

The ultimate aim of self-understanding is not just the gaining of insight, valuable as it is, but the achievement of more mature everyday living.

13.

Make Peace with Yourself

SELF-ESTEEM · ACCEPT YOURSELF
COMMON BARRIERS TO FRIENDLY RELATIONS
PRESUPPOSE FRIENDLINESS
FOR EMOTIONAL MATURITY

BEING human, we tend to blame our difficulties on everything and everybody except ourselves, but when we learn to evaluate our personalities, we may come to the conclusion that many of our troubles stem from our own unconscious attitudes. We may have inherited them ready-made from our families and our early environment, and they simply don't fit us any more. When we become aware of this, we will not be chained completely to our past.

We have the capacity to change but we must realize that we can do it only gradually. We have a strong tendency to hold onto set ways and fail to allow sufficient time in which to modify our behavior. Consequently, we are likely to become discouraged and confused.

Our first step should be to realize that we live in a changing world and must change with it. We need to allow ourselves a measure of flexibility so we can adjust easily to new situations. It helps to remember that Nature never

112

stands still, and is moving always toward normality and growth. If we are in rhythm with Nature, *the inherent order of things is in our favor.*

SELF-ESTEEM

In the process of checking up on our attitudes, we are usually so concerned with *devaluating* ourselves that we are likely to underestimate our potentialities. Too frequently for instance we lose sight of our innate good judgment because of our feelings of inadequacy, self-deprecation, fear, lack of confidence, or perhaps the lack of simple courage to follow through on some of our reasonable hunches. Low self-esteem often impels us to say, "If *I* thought of it, it can't be good." When we discover that some great person has said or written something similar, our sleepy self-esteem wakes up. These insights into the reasons for our behavior may come suddenly and dramatically, or we may achieve them less spectacularly by consciously evaluating our experiences. One way is to examine our reactions to past situations.

Try recalling your judgment of the behavior of friends and relatives in a certain situation. In the light of subsequent events, how good was your judgment; how correct your prediction? If your estimate was faulty, what had you failed to take into consideration? By carefully avoiding the human tendency of being wise in retrospect, you can arrive at a fairly accurate estimate of the soundness of your judgment.

ACCEPT YOURSELF

A certain amount of self-esteem is not only healthy but necessary, because it enables you to live comfortably with yourself and also to get along well with other people. If you are confused and full of self-blame, you will subconsciously express your frustration by faultfinding and blaming others. Constant criticism of others gives you a plausible excuse for your own immature behavior.

We must allow ourselves and others a margin of error, recognizing that no one is one hundred per cent perfect. Contemplate the sad situation in which humanity so often finds itself. Realize how frequently the wisest and best men of all ages, including our own, have acted without discernment and without real understanding. Consider the catastrophes and tragedies that have occurred on a world scale throughout the centuries, and then ask yourself, "Who am I to feel so terribly guilty for having made some mistakes, or done some childhood or adolescent wrongs?"

So hasten to make peace with yourself. Look critically at your guilty feelings about your minor omissions and commissions. They really aren't important enough to warrant the distress they cause you. Most likely, your feeling of guilt is a hang-over from your childhood in which parental authority took a condemning attitude toward most of your natural activities. "You mustn't do this," "You mustn't do that," "You mustn't get dirty," "That isn't nice," "You are bad." No wonder so many of us grew up with an uneasy feeling that everything we do is wrong.

Now that you are able to take a mature, realistic view of your minor frailties, you can give them their proper value. The peace of mind that comes with the acceptance of yourself as you are not only lessens nervous tensions but releases your energies for self-improvement. Particularly if you have an "extra-super-perfectionist" self-condemning conscience, self-acceptance is a special "must."

Self-acceptance is not only based upon the fundamental moral law, "Love thy neighbor as thyself," but also upon the latest psychological concepts. These concepts simply imply that everyone does and should love himself. Lack of love for our neighbor may often result from the fact that we don't sufficiently accept and love *ourselves*. The person who doesn't "like" himself is overcome by his inadequacies and his feeling of worthlessness. He is disappointed with himself; as a result appalling inferiority and self-hate are aroused, and may ultimately overwhelm him. His strong feeling of self-disparagement being thus reinforced, he may believe it is futile to make any attempt to change. This is a blind denial of the forces of life and progress at their very birth.

Unless we have a high esteem for ourselves we will not hate our unworthy traits and will not be too zealous in our efforts toward self-improvement. (WHILE SELF-ACCEPTANCE IS A VIRTUE, IT MUST NOT BE AN END IN ITSELF. NOR MUST IT BE ALLOWED TO MASQUERADE AS APATHY OR SELF-APPEASE-MENT.) Self-acceptance can give you the power to "pull yourself up by your own bootstraps." So like yourself in spite of your shortcomings.

Through self-acceptance, you put a stop to useless wishful thinking about what you could or should have been, or what you could or should have done. You organize your thoughts in the more realistic channels of what you can do *now* with all the assets that you possess.

This process is the essence of self-acceptance. You build up those assets and faculties that you possess to the point of such obvious worth that they glitter, and consequently submerge and diminish that part of your personality of which you are not proud. It is always easier to use your energies in building upon the solid foundations of your positive attributes.

Furthermore, when we have made peace with ourselves, we will find that we are able to take in our stride the usual everyday frustrations and obstructions. We then realize that all pressures and tensions incidental to living cannot be removed. Life is not constituted that way. It has rough steep hills as well as smooth level roadbeds.

An active and wholesome life is developed through *resisting* the oppressive forces and stresses under which we all must live. The person who tries to evade inevitable hard knocks is attempting to escape life itself. This can't be done! Rather, our thoughts and efforts should be concentrated on strengthening ourselves physically, emotionally, and morally, so as to be resilient enough to absorb the vicissitudes of life. Then our difficulties will no longer ruin our digestion, twitch our nerves, or make our blood boil. As the feeling of insecurity disappears, we do not need to keep up our defenses against a host of things that used to irritate us.

Finally, we learn that most of the threats to our happiness come from within ourselves. We have been quaking at monsters created by our own imagination. What a relief to know that *no one can hurt us as much as we can hurt ourselves.* This presents a challenge for us to change.

COMMON BARRIERS TO FRIENDLY RELATIONS

With the attainment of emotional maturity, you will find that you have also bettered your relations with other people. *The more you increase your capacity for liking people, the happier you are.*

And check your progress to make sure that your attitude toward your neighbors encourages them *to like you.* Do you consider the other fellow's feelings and opinions? Have you a sympathetic understanding of what makes him act as he does toward you? Perhaps he is harsh or irritable when he has no real intention of hurting you. He may simply be reacting to a private disturbance of which you are unaware. Or you may resemble someone he likes or dislikes for fairly sound reasons. He may be prejudiced or

timid or be one of those people who have met with disappointments and so hold back their friendship for fear
of getting hurt again. As soon as a relationship becomes
interesting, they drift away from it.

Maybe the other person finds your mannerisms annoying.
Are you aware of your own disturbing personality traits,
such as chronic complaining, aggressiveness, or self-
centeredness? Despite your best intentions, you may show
such traits to those with whom you associate. It is also
unfortunately possible that other persons may misconstrue
your motives. These are just a few of the many barriers
inhibiting friendships.

Again you may also irritate others without being aware
of it, not so much because of what *you* do or are, but because of *their* current condition or reactions. For example,
if you are calm while they are excited, your very calmness
may annoy them, and vice versa. If you have never had a
headache, you cannot understand the other fellow's misery.
When your stomach is full, you do not fully appreciate the
other fellow's hunger. Likewise, a starved man cannot
easily comprehend the relaxed state of the well-fed.

If you are honest with yourself (it never pays to be
otherwise!), you recognize that your difficulties with other
people may stem *in part* from your wrong inner attitudes
toward them.

For instance, you may feel insecure and express your
insecurity by shyness, timidity, embarrassment, or even
excessive aggressiveness. You can overcome these uneasy
feelings by realizing that almost all people feel as insecure
as you do.

The more intimately you participate in the life of any
group, the more you can see the other fellow's weaknesses.
By the same token, the more you assume social responsibilities, the more you discover your latent strength and

abilities. You become aware that you are as good as the next fellow in some respects, and that some of your good traits balance or overbalance your inadequacies. You perceive also that these same relations hold good for other people. With a little training, you can develop a self-confidence that will prevent others from hurting you, an inner strength that will help you "take" the unpleasantnesses that arise at times in almost any human relationship.

PRESUPPOSE FRIENDLINESS

A practical way to get along with people is to presume that they are disposed to be friendly rather than hostile. If you expect hostility, you are likely to arouse it. The other person may have the same uncertainties regarding you that you have toward him. However, if you show friendliness and warmth, he is more likely to respond in kind.

Show your feeling of good will toward others by your willingness to listen, by acting in a way calculated to please them, and by avoiding action you believe would not be to their liking. The maintenance of a true friendship is in some respects like playing a game of cards. You play not only according to what you have in your hand, but according to the nature of the other fellow's response. When you consider only what *you* want to do, *your* plans, wishes, and desires, and overlook the fact that your friend also has allied problems, plans, wishes, and ideas, it is infinitely more difficult for friendship to endure.

If you realize that there are some features about your friend that are not to your liking, and that he will continue to be his own individual self, be satisfied that you have *something* in common. But reserve for yourself, as well as for your friend, the right to withdraw from each other in those fields where you haven't much in common. Such a tolerant attitude can gradually reduce most of the tensions of friendship.

Finally, here are a few general rules that make for successful living.

FOR EMOTIONAL MATURITY

1. Seek more self-understanding.
2. Learn to control your likes and dislikes.
3. Resolve that you will make the necessary changes in attitudes toward yourself and your fellow man.
4. Co-operate in the welfare of the community, state, nation, and world in which you live.
5. Set the best possible example by mature behavior.
6. Be faithful in both thoughts and deeds to your basic spiritual values.

14.

Relax on the Job

THE RELAXED WAY OF DOING THINGS
COMMON CAUSES OF OCCUPATIONAL FATIGUE
AND TENSIONS
WHAT DOES YOUR JOB MEAN TO YOU?
HOW RELAXATION CAN HELP YOU WORK

FOR more than four decades, industrial psychologists have experimented in many kinds of industries to determine what value there is in *intermittent* rest periods, and if they are helpful in raising work efficiency. The results of all these tests have been practically unanimous; that brief regular rest periods increase the work output of employees and reduce accident hazards.

The rest period is usually spent sitting down if the work is performed in a standing position; or standing or strolling if the work requires sitting. Drinking a light beverage, smoking a cigarette, taking a walk, talking to associates, reading, listening to music, etc.—these are the usual means through which we expect to find relaxation from our tiring activities.

But they are not sufficiently restful to satisfy the need of a *fatigued* person. Industrial psychologists have not stressed how to achieve the most efficient way to complete rest in the shortest possible time.

The method here described is the first designed to give the fatigued individual the maximum physical and mental relaxation on the job *within a space of ten minutes!*

Here's how: During your rest period, utilize your stretch reflex exercise to the fullest extent. If convenient, lie down and follow through the abbreviated form of relaxation found on pages 41 and 42. Otherwise, in the sitting position, stretch the particular muscles that have been under stress or strain; also exercise the muscles of your neck. Take several yawns. Gently massage your temples and forehead. Spend about a minute in wriggling all the muscles of your body. Get yourself into the most comfortable position. Start slow, rhythmic breathing. Quiet every muscle group in your body and every operation of your mind through the continuous use of the control word, "quiet."

After this take a brief mental vacation. Simply close your eyes, and mentally go back to some former pleasant happening or occasion. You will find no difficulty in evoking the most distant or soothing scene from the treasures of your memory. Linger over the "happy view" until your face and eye muscles feel relieved, and your nerves are quieted. As you open your eyes again, you should find yourself refreshed, and this simple restorative practice will repay you in dividends of increased activity. Ten minutes spent in doing this and in *doing nothing else* will banish much of your fatigue and mental tension.

THE RELAXED WAY OF DOING THINGS

Paradoxical as it may sound, there are also ways to relax while you are actually working. And, moreover, by learning and practicing the easiest way of doing your particular job, you will work better and faster. Analyze your occupational movements. When your work requires you to use your body in one position, then stretch yourself in the opposite position so as to equalize the muscular pull. How much of your body do you use and how much do you need to use? Do you have the needed equipment within easy reach? Are you employing muscles that do not need to be employed or twisting your body into awkward, tiring postures? If so, you are not only lessening your efficiency by these superfluous movements, but you will become unnecessarily fatigued and strained.

Think about it, and you will be able to see that most of your work can be performed by using only the needed part of the body, and all your other muscles can be relatively at rest. If you are writing at a desk, for instance, it is not necessary to hunch your shoulders and twist your legs around the chair. Only the fingers are needed for typing; you may invite neuritis by tensing your wrists, arms, and the muscles of your neck. Apply the principle of mechanical leverage to your movements. It is poor muscular economy to lift a heavy object when you could more easily drag it, or pull it when it is easier to push.

Before attempting to lift any heavy object, have all the muscles of your body under control. You accomplish that by first taking a deep breath, then immediately lifting the object. By doing so, you take advantage of the strength of your powerful leg and thigh muscles. If you lift when your muscles are not under control, you expose yourself to possible groin or back strain.

In this connection, here are some RULES TO KNOW, as contained in the United States Department of Labor, Bulletin No. 113:

1. Look over the object to decide the best way to grasp it.
2. Place your feet close to the object to be lifted.

3. Get a good grip on the load.
4. Bend your knees—keep your back straight.
5. Keep the load close to your body.
6. Be sure you can see past the load.
7. Get help for large or heavy objects.
8. In team lifting—co-operate with your buddy.

Check up often on your breathing. Is it normal or is it shallow? If you are coasting along lethargically on a light chest breathing instead of filling your lungs by a fuller movement of the diaphragm, you may not be getting enough oxygen. This would account for your feeling dull and let down. Try a little deep breathing and see how quickly you become wide awake and alert, with all your reactions and perceptions sharpened.

So far, we have been talking about muscular economy. But in addition, many of us burn up much more mental energy than the job requires. We impulsively open our mental spigot wide and then with a disconcerting splurge, out flows tremendous splashing power, in the form of nerve-wracking confusion, unnecessary excitement, or panicky fretting.

Each of us should become aware of the normal tempo at which we work best, the point on our own particular rhythmostat at which we can keep up a steady efficient pace with the least fatigue. Our work is then performed in smooth, free-flowing, rhythmic muscular movements, and our mental processes are under complete control. But when our job becomes annoying or fatiguing, we can ease those tensions by stopping what we are doing for a few minutes, to do or think about something else. Welcome this occasional break in your work tempo. It always helps.

You can also train yourself into relaxation by getting up slowly instead of impulsively, walking methodically in good posture, breathing rhythmically, and sitting down slowly. As you stop rushing and hurrying, your anxiety is correspondingly reduced.

In addition you will find that the deliberate controlled change of pace and the brief respite is an excellent way to clear your mind of confusion. These little breathing spells help you to put your thoughts in order.

The following simple practices will help to restore your poise and bring you quick relaxation while you are on your job:

1. Work at something else for a little while.
2. Occasionally permit your *entire* body to become limp and at ease.
3. Consider interruptions as *opportunities* for a breathing spell and mental stocktaking.
4. Take frequent short "mental vacations."

COMMON CAUSES OF OCCUPATIONAL FATIGUE AND TENSIONS

The following is only a partial list of the common fatigue-producing factors associated with many a job. Checking these will help to give you a picture of your attitude to your work. You alone can tell which factors apply to you. The recognition of any source of tension is the first step to its elimination.

1. Overwork; excessively long or hard labor.
2. Lack of interest.
3. Boredom because of unstimulating or insufficient work.
4. Occupational distortions produced by poor posture or faulty work movements.
5. Lack of appreciation for your efforts.

6. Feeling that your work doesn't call forth your true capabilities.

7. Friction involving fellow workers, "customers," or management.

8. Poor state of general health.

9. Emotional upsets or "worries."

10. Wrong attitude toward your work or fellow worker; faulty philosophy.

11. Poor working conditions—inadequate illumination, noise, fumes, poor ventilation, heat or cold, cleanliness, crowded quarters, poor equipment, etc.

12. Unattractive, unhealthy, or time-consuming commuting.

Everyday interruptions are another cause of tension. While it is not always possible to ignore them, you can lessen the force of their impact if you consider them not as robbers of time but an opportunity to relax.

The methods of easing tension that we have listed will be helpful to you if you know the causes of your fatigue. They are not so effective in relieving the fatigue that comes from emotional maladjustment to your work, or other hidden factors that spring from deeper dissatisfaction. Nevertheless, *every period of complete rest is a definite gain.* At least it frees you temporarily from some of the nerve-wracking aspects of your work.

After a period of relaxation, you may be better able to tolerate minor annoyances (they exist everywhere) and to find the maximum of contentment on your job. You may see how to better distressing conditions or make up your mind to endure those that cannot be changed. By clearing your mind of confusing tensions, you will be better able to analyze your job and determine what is at the root of your problems as well as what you should do about it.

WHAT DOES YOUR JOB MEAN TO YOU?

First of all, what is your goal? What do you expect to accomplish within the next ten years? The next twenty? Is your present job a means toward reaching that goal or is it merely a stopgap? Perhaps your goals are not connected with your work, and you desire only that it should be a more or less pleasant and adequate way of earning a living. Whatever your job means to you, is it doing what you expect of it? Think carefully about the favorable and unfavorable conditions connected with it and compare them with conditions you may reasonably expect to find in another situation. And try as far as possible, to be realistic in your job analysis. Too many of us are persistently trying to escape reality, longing to live and work in a world of our own imagining. Of course, we have the *right*—and to some extent, the personal and social *obligation*—to seek the most ideal conditions, but we must put these conditions that we dream about to the test of what is possible and obtainable. Otherwise, we find ourselves in an even less satisfactory job situation than the one which we formerly deplored.

Now suppose, after casting up your mental balance sheet, you find that the job is moderately satisfactory, how do you feel about the work itself? There are boring and tiresome aspects to every job; these cannot be avoided and so should be discounted. But the over-all performance of your work should give you a sense of satisfaction. Your job should not be so perplexing as to cause you continual fear of failure. Nor should it be so easy and uninteresting that you will tend to develop a casual and sloppy attitude toward it.

A sheer *dislike of your work* is one of the most common causes of tension. The remedy is either a change of occupation or a change of attitude. The latter is much more difficult to achieve but worth considering before you rush off to make a change. For the root of your dissatisfaction with the work may be in your own personality. Your tensions may be induced *on the job*, through your irritation with fellow workers, superiors, or the pattern of the daily work itself. These same self-made tensions you would probably carry with you and transfer to any other job. With a changed perspective, you may come to see that many of your occupational problems are of minor importance.

A feeling that you are merely a "cog in a wheel" and will never amount to anything is a depressing attitude and therefore a generator of fatigue. But did you ever consider that if your job does not require all of your mental and physical energy, your mind is freed for other things? When your work is semiautomatic, you can surely put some of your thoughts to work productively. Perhaps you can make improvement in your job. The intelligent workman knows or can discover much more about a given procedure than those who supervise or theorize about it.

Many people find a never-ending source of interest in the dramas of their fellow workers. While your hands are performing their given task, your mind and your sympathies may be engaged in friendly, neighborly contact with the man at the next machine or desk. After all, you spend a great part of your waking hours at work and this is the time to make friends and establish a good rapport with life.

Never underestimate the worth of your own labors. If you begin a task with the notion that *the job is too easy*, you may overestimate your ability and with bravado say, "Oh, there's nothing to it." Suppose you set yourself a time limit. If the work takes a few minutes extra, you fall into the nervous trap that you have set for yourself. You blame yourself for inefficiency when in reality it is only your calculation that had been faulty. You brood. Your nervous tension mounts. Every additional minute seems an hour because it is a threat to your self-esteem.

Or you may fall into the mental attitude that *you are not capable of performing the work,* or that it will take you forever. Thus you start with a handicap of impatience. The notion that the job is beyond you, immediately ties you into knots. Then, no matter how smoothly the work may proceed, you have so conditioned yourself to expecting hardships that you suffer unnecessary misgivings and set up inevitable tensions.

To give yourself a better perspective about your work, remember that *it does not help to punish yourself mentally for all that you don't accomplish.* You may be setting yourself an impossibly fast pace. As a general rule, what keeps you tired and tense is not so much the load of actual physical work as the *increased "mental rushing."* Your mind speeds faster than your hands or feet; your feelings suffer from the resultant disharmony in tempo. It is better to find contentment in what you *can* do and in what you already have accomplished, recognizing that the tasks remaining are eventually capable of fulfillment.

It may help to make a list of the principal things you need or wish to do. In this way you will free your mind of the possibility of forgetting important items. You will also see the Unfinished Business ahead, and will note at a glance what you have already achieved. Such stocktaking, checking off what you have finished in relation to what still remains to be done, can furnish you with comfort and satisfaction.

Above all, do not approach your work as though it were a necessary evil, a hateful form of drudgery, just an enforced means of earning your living. Those who hold this attitude do the smallest possible amount of work, and then brag about their ability to make their employers think they're working diligently. They usually come home exhausted not so much from their unappetizing work as from their persistent inner discontent.

On the other hand, you should not expect too much of yourself. It is poor economy to whip yourself to the breaking point to finish a job on time. Don't become like a wound-up watch, set to run fast. When the engine of your organism runs at top speed, you wear yourself out prematurely, and ultimately your efficiency suffers.

Often we expect more of ourselves than the most critical outsider. In our overanxiety to succeed, we drive ourselves on and on. We overestimate our abilities or we fear that the job is beyond us. The basic cure for these and many other aspects of job fatigue is to work in a relaxed way. As a matter of fact, taking a pause to cool off—physically and emotionally—will tend to slow you down to a rational, healthful, and efficient pace.

Driving yourself to the point of exhaustion so that later you will have *more* time to relax is not only foolish, but exceedingly dangerous to your well-being. You will be on edge, taut, and irritable. Then too, you may find it harder to relax when you finally have the opportunity to do so. Moreover, when you are keyed up, additional or unexpected demands become so hard to meet that you are likely to "blow your top." Later, you will realize that your state of tension was chiefly responsible for the brain storm.

Never fail to appreciate the worth of your labors. Practically any task has an immediate significance as well as a lasting value. An understanding of the *broader meaning* of what you do to earn your living helps to sustain your faith in the merit of your work.

HOW RELAXATION CAN HELP YOU WORK

1. It increases your efficiency.
2. It heightens your alertness.
3. It enlivens your interest in your work.
4. It makes you less accident-prone.
5. It decreases your fatigue.
6. It reduces your nervousness.
7. It helps you to retain, arouse, or develop a sense of humor and good will.
8. It furthers the development of physical and mental health.
9. It betters the relationship between yourself and your fellow workers.
10. It makes you happier in your outlook.

A period of occupational relaxation has a balancing or steadying influence upon your feelings and emotions. If you are *depressed,* the ability to relax makes it easier for you to pull yourself up out of your gloom. When you are excessively *elated,* relaxing helps you come down to earth more quickly. If you are *agitated,* relaxing gives you precious time to recover from wounded sensitivity or hurt feelings. So universally useful a tool as relaxation should be kept available to help you to meet a variety of your needs.

15.

Relax at Play

WHAT KIND OF PLAY?

IN THIS age of high pressure, we all need to relax at play. It doesn't matter whether we play at something constructive or something that merely gives us entertainment as long as it helps us release our inner tensions. What *is* important is that we should have variety enough to save us from boredom. And so we should preserve both the sort of hobbies or games that takes us out of the home, and others which we can follow inside our own homes.

Hobbies, as a rule, are more fun when they *contrast* with our work, but we needn't choose them deliberately for that purpose. The more hobbies or diversions we cultivate, the more interesting life becomes, provided we do not take them too seriously, and also that we choose those best suited to our age, health and temperament.

The important thing about hobbies is that they should

be fascinating enough to engage our minds as well as our physical energies. When we become so proficient at a hobby that is only physical exercise and we find our unemployed minds dwelling on our troubles, that hobby has lost its meaning for us. It is time to look for something more absorbing.

OUTDOOR RECREATION

Opportunities for outdoor recreation are limited only by our interests. Tennis, for instance, if one is young and spry enough, gives the muscles a splendid workout. The skill required for the game and the quick strategic decisions give us also a keen mental pleasure.

Golf, less strenuous and better adapted to the middle-aged, develops muscular co-ordination and a nice sense of timing. It is a social game for those who enjoy their friends as much as the sport.

Or perhaps you may have a preference for the more solitary sports, such as walking, skating, or fishing. Skating offers one outstanding advantage, it is a sport in which you can indulge even when you grow old—if you keep it up. The fun begins as soon as you are able to stand on skates and it is even more fun as you learn to attune your body to the perfect rhythm this recreation demands. It is a peculiarly satisfying physical exercise and gives you the opportunity for endless advancement toward perfection.

Walking is as healthful as it is enjoyable. When you saunter along a quiet lane in the park or in the woods, in rhythm with nature, you attain a feeling of humility and peace.

If you are a fisherman, you have, no doubt, learned that after baiting the hook and throwing it in the water, there is a lazy interval in which to enjoy the play of light and shade on the water. Perhaps you have observed a grasshopper near you on the bank; how he jumps and rests, rests and jumps. His built-in rhythmostat is working perfectly. He is obeying the basic law of nature—animated activity, alternating with purposeful repose.

Almost any kind of outing can be fun; you may find you prefer it to planned sport. Taking your children on a picnic, a trip to the circus, a ride to the beach, or the park, is the pleasantest sort of entertainment. And if you have no children, there are many crippled youngsters, sick veterans, or aged folk who need a little simple fun in their lives. Such moderate activity helps you to avoid the danger of *the disease of excess ease*—one of the worst maladies to which human flesh is subject.

FUN INDOORS

The whole range of esthetic pursuits has exceptional relaxation value. When you are singing, painting, or modeling you do not think of *yourself*, and if you are one of a group, you completely forget yourself. Incidentally, painting is an excellent means of expressing disturbing emotions and has been used widely for this purpose. Even solitary dancing to the rhythm of phonograph music in the privacy of your own room can bring temporary relief from mounting tensions.

When you become completely absorbed in music, whether singing, playing or composing, you are freed from inner stress. You may remain bodily in the same drab hole in the wall but your spirit is freed. And when you become skillful enough to perform publicly with others, you enjoy being a part of a trained group. The strengthening influence of such an experience is deep and lasting.

Although you may not be a musician, when you notice that certain music comforts you, give yourself to it *wholeheartedly;* get completely into the rhythm or swing of it.

Let your imagination *lift your spirit high,* above what you believe to be your humdrum life.

The *recollection* of music also can be soothing. As you hear it with your memory, you re-experience the original pleasure. Its beauty, even its vagueness, may free you momentarily at least from the workaday burdens that generate stress. But do not let these vague delights unduly enthrall you. After a reasonable period, break away from them and take up some *active* recreation.

RECREATION AT HOME

Many doctors urge the nervous parent to interest himself in the projects of children—his own or others. Sharing the interests of the young is not only a way of retaining a youthful spirit, but is a sure cure for the blues.

Launching in the home a group project, such as weaving, modeling or carpentering, can often make family life much more interesting. Perhaps Mother is making a hooked rug. If she leaves the frame in the living-room where the whole family can see it, Little Sister may want to put in a cloud or a tree. Even Father may try his hand at filling in a roof or a chimney.

A few tools and a workbench in the basement provide entertainment for many a rainy Sunday. Carpentering can become an absorbing occupation that requires not only skill and accuracy but a sense of design. Gardening, house painting, redecorating, any of the chores of keeping up a home, can be made an entertaining family project.

Then too, one of the pleasantest ways of cementing family solidarity and at the same time forgetting one's own problems is games. When the whole family plays any game from anagrams to samba, they are strengthening the habit of enjoying each other. It is hard to nurse a grouch or retire into a mood of depression when one is matching his wits against his brothers and sisters in friendly competition.

TOLERANCE

Perhaps you have noticed that whether you are playing games or pursuing a hobby, you cannot have fun if you insist on being a perfectionist. You will enjoy your hobby only so long as you are not too concerned about finishing your undertaking on time or about making it as perfect as you had hoped. If it's a game it may not be as much fun as you expected, but you can still get some pleasure out of it, especially when you don't care whether you win or lose. The point is to extract all the relaxation value from what you are doing.

If cards bore you, by all means avoid them. Taking a hand in a game merely to please others is certain to irritate you, not to mention your partner. Conversely, if you insist on somebody else's playing a game that doesn't entertain him, you need not expect him to be overpolite.

Of course, for the sake of peace between friends or within the family, as well as to maintain our own standards of good conduct, we have to be agreeable. So once in a while uninviting recreation may be looked upon as a task that has to be done. By adopting toward it the attitude that "this, too, shall pass," we are often surprised to find ourselves enjoying it. At least we set a mature example of co-operation.

Indeed, co-operation and a companionable attitude are more necessary in recreation than in many other aspects of our daily lives. If we want to enjoy a friend we must learn to overlook his or her idiosyncrasies that we find hard to tolerate. We can enjoy together activities that we both like, then separate unhesitatingly when there is no common interest. Mathematically, we cannot expect to find many people who will like *everything* we like. Even so, a rewarding friendship need not be interrupted just because we have little in common; for real friendships are rare and they certainly help us to enjoy life. The more good friends we have, the better!

SERVICE TO OTHERS

If you aren't interested in sports or a hobby, you may find relaxation and enjoyment in the activities of your church or club, even your political organization. Volunteer work offers many possibilities, depending on your preference and skill—from taking care of your neighbor's baby while she goes shopping, to training others in a major craft.

Helping those who are less fortunate than you are is a sure way of escape from boredom or from the repetitiousness of a humdrum existence. Unselfish and joyful giving of yourself can be the best of fun.

WHY NOT SOMETHING DIFFERENT?

Our usual modes of entertainment are far too standardized and monotonous. Why not try something different? Instead of always going out in the car, it might be amusing to try a bike for a change. If you haven't been riding a bicycle for some time, you will be pleased with your self-made speed and you will enjoy the invigorating breeze you yourself have created.

Be daring enough to try horseback riding—but for a starter, pick out a horse as old as you are!

If your youngsters invite you to go along on a ski trip, you too can enjoy it, even if you don't succeed in following them up hill and down dale.

Be brave enough to go on the merry-go-round or giant roller coaster. If courage fails you, treat a child—and go along for the ride.

The spirit of adventure is dormant in each one of us. We may not be able to climb Mount Everest, but we can find plenty of new and exciting experiences if we only look for them. Such activities will give us far more satisfaction than in listening *passively* to a nightly radio program or patronizing a neighborhood movie house.

HOW NOT TO PLAY

Watching some of our friends, neighbors or family allegedly "enjoying" themselves, we sometimes get the idea that their play is painfully hard work. They concentrate so fiercely that they grow taut, their nerves are on edge, and they can stand no interruptions from the most loving member of the family. They even resent a mild shift in the conversation.

How often have you visited friends who are "relaxing" from their daily worries by watching television? Do not expect a warm and friendly greeting, especially from a *new* television owner; hospitality leaves as the set enters. You are told hastily to "take a chair and sit down quietly." The show must go on!

Or friends invite you to spend a "quiet" evening playing cards. You find them with muscles taut, jaws set, spines stiff as a ramrod, eyes popping, alert for the slightest mistake of a partner. All they need is a holster and a gun to re-enact an old Western gambling scene.

Or perhaps you have been lured into a game of golf or tennis with a partner who is so intent on winning that he is critical, almost belligerent. Your nerves become so jangled trying not to make a bad play and let him down that you end the game in a state of mental exhaustion.

But are you sure that when *you* yourself undertake some project you do not go at it with the *same grim determination?*

Perhaps you may decide to do some redecorating in your home. You say, "It's going to be fun, and it won't take long." So you commence your work in good spirits, hopefully expecting that it will be a cinch. But soon you are driving yourself to finish a certain amount in a given time, fuming at interruptions and delays. Consequently, you not only do a sloppy job but you are an irritable nervous wreck as well. However the redecorating would have been fun and the pleasant relaxation you counted on, if you hadn't cared how much or when you got done.

When the chief aim is to enjoy yourself, all that is necessary is to have a *relaxed attitude* toward whatever you are doing. Details of the game, instructions as to how a hobby should be carried out, how a toy should work need not overly concern you. If you take these things too seriously, you sacrifice the end to the means. For an easy mind and a freely relaxed body, the best approach to your games and hobbies is a "take-it-or-leave-it" attitude.

THE RHYTHMOSTAT IN RECREATION

As we have seen, there is a *self-regulating* limit to all of our moods, actions, and inactions. If we work too much, we need to play. If we play too much, we need to rest. If we overrest, we need to be active again. When we understand this law and are attuned to it, we will have learned how to get the most from relaxation.

Our vitality and reserve energy determine whether we can safely force ourselves to go on playing, or whether we should compensate our fatigue with rest. It is sometimes hard to tell whether fatigue is caused by inertia or boredom or whether it is an acute cry of the body tissues for rest. If boredom is making us tired, a slight positive stimulation can shake it off. For even though we may be physically tired to the point of exhaustion yet suddenly we become living dynamos when stimulated by a challenge to our self-esteem or a response to a romantic interest. But when we don't know *why* we are tired, it is prudent to relax.

16.

Relaxed-Alert Driving

THE HUMAN ELEMENTS · FELLOW DRIVERS
RELAXED-ALERT DRIVING · SMILE AS YOU DRIVE
WHAT KIND OF SMILE · WHAT A SMILE WON'T DO
WHAT A SMILE WILL DO
THE ULTIMATE SOLUTION TO SAFE DRIVING

THE HUMAN ELEMENTS

Is IT safe or practical to relax while driving? If you are relaxed, can you still be "alert"? The answer to both questions is "yes." In this chapter we will describe a relaxed-alert state that will lessen the possibility of your having a road accident. First, however, let us consider the human elements most frequently involved.

Much that can be said about the accident-prone driver is equally true of *accident-prone pedestrians*. Many haphazard jaywalkers are completely indifferent to life. Others adopt too literally the attitude of "this is my country," and they insist on this right at any time and any place. They are so "brave" and "daring" that they will even die to defend their rights as "free" American citizens. And then there is a group of naïve, trusting souls who assume that the brakes of *all* cars are *always* well-adjusted and will *always* hold.

Strange as it may seem, some people deliberately, though probably unconsciously, want to *get hurt a little bit*, so that they can get sympathy, cash in on compensation and sick benefits, or relieve themselves of some responsibility. But it is too much to expect that the motorist will understand their subconscious objective. And the law is no kinder to the unfortunate driver than nature is to his victim.

Again many traffic accidents are caused by *overwrought emotions*. Mr. Herbert J. Stack, Director of the New York University Center for Safety Education, maintains that chronic traffic violations do not result from lack of driving *ability* so much as they do from poor driving *personality*. When we are behind the wheel our personality defects have a speedy and ugly chance to assert themselves, perhaps because we have at our command such a lethal weapon.

Our highways are the battlegrounds of our emotions. The driver's fear, anger, hate, malice, vanity, jealousy, selfishness, greed, distrust, dominance, dependence, exhibitionism, aggressiveness—to list but a few common mental states—are all easily visible in his driving. Bumper-to-bumper driving may even reflect the "instinct" of gregariousness! His inhibitions no longer keep him in check. Emotional irritations are unleashed by pressure on the accelerator. Anxiety expresses itself in excessive speed. *Nervous tension and fast driving inevitably go hand in hand.*

FELLOW DRIVERS

Recognizing the fellow traveler who is driving the car ahead of you, or the driver pushing you from behind, trying to find a few inches in which to squeeze past, helps you to be forewarned about what he is going to do.

There is the *teen-age* driver, for instance, who dashes

ahead with zest and immaturity, determined to make speed.
Rules of the road mean nothing to him and traffic regula-
tions are a nuisance. Be wary of him for he is a superhazard.
Insurance companies consider him an extra risk.

The *slow poke* ambles at his own pace, usually that of a
snail, no matter how many cars are behind him or how wide-
open the road is ahead. Dulled by the hypnotic hum of the
motor, sunk into the cushiony comfort of his seat, he rolls
along in a state of lethargy. His slow reflexes are the cause
of many an accident.

The *show-off* must always be proving something. If he
is driving a new car, he must demonstrate its speed. If it
is an old one, he must prove that his outmoded model is
just as powerful as the newest one on the road. He is always
in a great hurry, so he zigzags in and out of the lanes, show-
ing how adroit he is and what he can do on two wheels,
how well he can miss collisions by a few inches and by split
seconds. His raucous horn and bright lights play "chop-
sticks" on your nerves. Usually he gets away with it.

The *trusting soul* is the driver who is always telling himself "Things will be all right," "Anyway, I'm insured," "God
will take care of me." He trusts that people will get out of
his way quickly, that children will not dash out between
cars, hopes the neglected brakes of his car—and other cars
—will hold, and believes that signals will always work. He
childishly depends on fate to guarantee that by some mira-
cle he will never be in an accident.

The *perfectionist* is another menace. He knows all about
his car and about the road. He is the perfect driver; therefore, he expects all others to be perfect. He unreasonably
relies upon the *other* driver to "do the right thing at the
right moment." He assumes that he has complete control
of himself and of his own machine. Technically, he is perfectly right, so he never gives an inch. If he meets with an

accident, it could not possibly have been *his* fault—it was the other fellow's. *He himself did the right thing.*

The *discontented driver* is the introvert who drives to work off the tensions of his repressions. He can't say to the boss what is really on his mind. He dares not talk back to his wife. He is not able to control his children. He usually fails to get the best of his business competitor. But when he is alone on the highway he becomes boss. He needs to "get even" for the many indignities he has suffered, so down goes his foot on the accelerator. Away he goes, tearing up the road, feeling the engine power throbbing under the hood, finding in speed an outlet for his accumulated griev-ances. At the wheel, if not at home or in the office or shop, he is the master of his fate. The only thing you can do when you meet him is to avoid him like the plague.

The *harassed father* out with his family, is one of the most erratic drivers on the road. His domestic boss demands that he go slower while the younger generation of back-seat drivers urges him to go faster and faster. He is buffeted by the contradictory emotions of the family boxed together with him in the cramped space and he finds an outlet for his confusion by pressing his big toe on the accelerator. His energies just naturally flow in that direction. Such confused drivers help to increase the high fatality rate of week-end driving.

RELAXED-ALERT DRIVING

If you are aware of all these fellow-driver hazards and they do not bother you; if you are that rare individual who has never suffered an accident, has *never* violated *any* traffic laws; is perfectly at ease and alert behind the wheel; and if, after reaching your destination, you usually feel rested and cheerful, then this chapter is not for you. But if you have been in accidents of your own or others' making; if you are the anxious driver, always on edge while at the wheel; or if, after a trip, you are greatly fatigued, then the following recommendations *can* be helpful to you.

1. To relax while driving does not mean that you sit in the car as relaxed as you would in an armchair by the fireplace at home; nor should you be lethargic, indifferent, or foolishly smug and sure of yourself. Actually you should be *both relaxed* and *alert*. To attain this ideal state of mind first be sure that you are comfortably seated in an *erect* posture. Do not permit yourself to droop in a slumped position, because this robs you of alertness. Your arms, shoulders, and neck muscles should be loose and limber and not stiff or firm.

2. When you are tired, make the most of traffic-signal stops. Even while at the wheel, you can stretch your whole body and yawn. You will find this amazingly refreshing. Then too you may shift your sitting position. Some drivers

A half-minute traffic light stretch. When traffic comes to a complete standstill, put on your hand brake and stretch the fatigue and tension of driving out of your entire body.

find it more comfortable to place a pillow or cushion under the buttocks or at the small of the back.

3. The relaxed-alert driver eases his mind by making sure (ahead of time) that his car has been put and kept in good mechanical condition.

4. When you are annoyed, disturbed, or agitated for any reason whatsoever, turn off the road to rest and "cool off." It is more senseless and infinitely *more dangerous to drive with overheated emotions than to drive with an overheated engine!* Guard yourself against such powerful feelings while driving. You can't safely and effectively control both strong emotions and the sensitive steering mechanism at the same time. Wearing a faint smile on your face will help you to relax sufficiently so that you will not be overcome by the heights of ecstasy, the depths of depression, or by any other intense experience.

4. After eating a heavy meal, it is advisable to rest a while before resuming a trip. Better yet, eat lightly before commencing or during a long journey.

5. Give yourself *extra* time to reach your destination, allowing for unexpected delays.

6. Do not look upon the first sign of fatigue or weariness as a challenge to your will power but rather as a warning to obey a vital safety rule. Get off the road at the very first opportunity, and rest until fatigue wears off. Make your body completely limp; close your eyes and mind to *everything*.

Taking a refreshing soft drink, a smoke, or a walk, while conceivably beneficial as an interruption, is insufficient. You need *complete* bodily relaxation, especially in the region of your eye muscles to free them from the tension, the glare, or the sheer monotony that arises from constant alertness in watching the road.

7. Do not expect other drivers to do what you would do

under certain circumstances. Give them the benefit of a margin of error. Allow for human weaknesses. Many drivers —including men—unwittingly signal or even go left when they want to turn right, and vice versa.

8. Do not assume that the other fellow will invariably obey even the most obvious traffic rules. Furthermore, keep in mind that the most normal person may momentarily suffer a slight dizzy attack, develop a sudden blind spot, black out when faced with a hard, unpleasant problem, fail to notice a change in the traffic light; or, if he happens to be angry and literally "sees red" (i.e., a traffic light), instead of slowing up or stopping he may merely go faster.

9. Allow for the carelessness of pedestrians. Those who do not own or drive a car often have little conception of the driver's problems and are unwilling to co-operate in a tight situation. Beware too of the accident-prone pedestrian, especially the young and the old.

10. Limit your speed! Provide for unforeseen mechanical failure and for mistakes in judgment—on your part and in others.

11. Avoid constant staring. Blink often. Permit your eye muscles to move frequently in their full range of vision, *without taking your eyes off the road*. Glance occasionally at the rear-view mirror and at the instrument panel. Occasionally move your head from side to side and up and down. This also removes much of your eye-muscle strain.

12. Establish the habit of Smiling as You Drive.

SMILE AS YOU DRIVE

Why does it help to smile as you drive? Because as soon as your eyes become strained tension sets in. With tension comes fatigue. When we are fatigued, good sense and sportsmanship fly out the window, road courtesy is forgotten, and irritability is heightened.

A smile relaxes the eye and face muscles, and when they are relaxed our brains are correspondingly more alert. Then too it takes far less energy and muscle play to smile than to be tense. It is organically impossible to have truly relaxed eye and facial muscles and yet be generally tense. The eyeball, of course, is the most important of all the human organs involved in driving. It is controlled by six intrinsic muscles, all of which are usually tense if accompanied by an unsmiling face. When those muscles become hypertense, vision is impaired to some degree. Nervousness is bound to follow, and then fatigue.

The eye exercises found in chapter 5 will help to overcome this condition.

WHAT KIND OF SMILE

The smile best suited to relaxed-alert driving is one that will *ease up* your eye muscles. It is not a dreamy smile, nor an exuberant or excited one; it isn't the sad wan smile of resignation, nor the smile of contempt or scorn. And of course the smirk that hides road murder in your soul won't do anyone any good. The *right* kind of smile is the one that will make you feel quietly contented yet alert.

If you keep a faint benevolent smile long enough, its influence spreads to your hands and feet, enhancing the normal speed and accuracy of your self-control and the coordination of your entire body.

Thoughtful smiling has a positive influence on the rest of your organism. To prove this try an experiment. Put a faint smile on your face, become quiet, and after a while note the radiating reaction spreading over your entire body.

WHAT A SMILE WON'T DO
(In Case You Don't Know!)

1. It will not chase away the highway patrolman.
2. It will not remove traffic controls.

3. It will not make the pedestrian jump out of your way.

4. It will not straighten out the curves of the road.

5. It will not adjust your brakes or other parts of the car mechanism.

6. It is not a perfect form of insurance against all possible road tragedies.

7. It will not prevent mistakes caused by ignorance or inadequate skill.

8. Your smile—or your fist—or your horn—won't influence the grossly careless driver or the psychopath of the road.

WHAT A SMILE WILL DO

1. Relax your eye muscles and every other feature of your face.

2. Make you more alert.

3. Lessen your haste.

4. Increase your compliance with traffic rules and regulations.

5. Decrease your impatience with all forms of road discourtesy.

6. Increase your own courtesy by encouraging friendlier attitudes.

7. Increase your passengers' trust in you.

8. Lessen your irritability and help to quiet your nerves.

9. Banish traces of depression.

10. Make your driving happier.

Adopt this motto:
Turn on your smile when you switch on your ignition!

THE ULTIMATE SOLUTION TO SAFE DRIVING

There is no quick and easy way to solve this complex problem. The heedless operator who refuses to conform to necessary traffic rules, ignores elementary road courtesy, drives while under the influence of alcohol or drugs, or permits his worst feelings to dominate him while behind the wheel is a far greater menace to every other person on the highway than bad roads or mechanical failures.

Greater road safety is not only to be obtained by better road conditions, but by inculcating in drivers—both young and old—a sense of obligation to others as well as disciplined self-restraint and self-respect. The highway accident rate, as well as the mental casualties which precede and help cause collisions, can best be reduced through personality re-education. The reason is clear: SOUND DRIVING IS SIMPLY *part* OF SOUND LIVING!

17.

Relax at Home

CAUSES OF TENSION IN THE HOUSEHOLD
THE DEMOCRATIC HOME · ENVIRONMENTAL AIDS
BLESSED BE THIS DOOR · CONQUERING NOISE

TRUE relaxation at home does not depend upon the easy chair or the soft life, nor upon physical fitness alone. It depends primarily upon a relaxed attitude toward yourself. *People who don't like themselves are never pleased with anything or anybody!* Dislike of yourself, when prolonged, makes you tense, and so you cause tenseness all around you.

CAUSES OF TENSION IN THE HOUSEHOLD

Some obvious causes of tension in the home are: excessive efficiency, supercleanliness, perfectionism, dominance, or exceptional exactitude. These attitudes represent "hangovers" in the home-maker's outlook from the days when she was working in office, factory, or classroom; or they may be brought home every day by the male breadwinner. Under such severe conditions, parents as well as children are kept in a constant state of neuromuscular tension by their attempt to "live up to" unusually strict "imported" patterns of controlled behavior.

149

Strangulating regulations can make a jail out of a home. If nothing worse, the least harm this does is to destroy the comfort, warmth, and "livability" of the home. Thus some meticulous but injudicious mothers attempt to make their house into a replica of the "model" magazine ads. Unfortunately everyone in the family feels as though he's on parade; the home becomes merely a place to eat and to sleep, a place where lounging is frowned upon.

THE DEMOCRATIC HOME

Genuine democracy in the home does not come about by accident. In such a home, both painful tensions and awkward silences are rare. Slaves or masters aren't found there. Every member has his basic duties, his rights, and his responsibilities. There is full family freedom of discussion followed by action according to a general consensus or majority rule. *Guidance but not dominance* is extended to the young. Each one "expresses" himself, perhaps grumbles a bit, but faithfully performs his necessary functions. The obstructionist idea of "I won't play" if others don't yield is completely foreign to this hearth. Infantile behavior is neither fostered nor tolerated. Harmonious living together means that there is a time for alternating dependence and independence, for mutual respect, guidance, love and understanding, and also for growth, development, discipline, and change.

The fulfilling of our responsibility to the family group does away with any need for the exercise of raw power. Each member *labors at this job of living together harmoniously*. The child has as much right to participate at his level as the elders. Details of parental decisions pertaining to the total family welfare are never arbitrarily imposed, but first discussed. Of course, there must be obedience, but it is understanding acceptance, not blind obedience. When there is occasion for reprimand or "discipline" in the narrow, negative sense, the parent administers it, but always ends the episode with some sign or word of affection. In the democratic home each person tries to do his part as a matter of course, without being coerced or applauded.

ENVIRONMENTAL AIDS

What *physical* improvements can you make in the house to achieve relaxed living? There are regular homemaking features in your favorite local newspaper, and monthly home magazines. But remember that material furnishings in the home should fit into the framework of easy living. Style, beauty, traditional artistic design, or novel esthetic tastes must not become substitutes for *the basic need for repose*. Here are a few hints:

1. Save your temper by arranging all your household appliances so that they can be easily found and easily reached.

2. A periodic resetting of the furnishings and pictures gives you a sense of surprise, newness, and freshness.

3. Chairs should be selected not only from the point of view of appearance, but also for maintaining or *bettering the posture* of the individual.

4. The bedroom. In small or crowded quarters, install a studio couch instead of the usual bed. Then that room, no matter how small, becomes a little private living room. Your bed or studio couch should comfortably fit the natural contours of your body; for this, a semi-firm mattress is usually indicated.

If your living quarters are crowded make better use of your available closets. A visit to the notions counter of your department store will reveal many gadgets you can install to help you find things at a moment's notice. You can also use hanging shelves to good advantage in making every inch of space count.

5. Color. Color has a strong effect upon our nerves, although we may not realize this. Naturally the living room should be decorated to meet the common taste of the family circle, but each bedroom—or personal "work retreat"—should fit the taste of the individual who occupies it.

6. Music. Where finances permit, equip each room with a radio. This makes it possible for each member of the family to enjoy his favorite programs without conflicting with the preferences of the others.

7. All rooms should be frequently ventilated.

8. Adjust the amount of light according to your individual need. Arrange the lamps so that the main light falls over the left shoulder.

9. Doors. *Privacy is the greatest single essential for relaxation.* Freedom from intruders depends upon *doors*. Archways rob you of privacy; doors restore it. If it is impossible or too expensive to install a needed door, at least give yourself the benefit of "makebelieve" privacy by screening off your part of the room. For some section of the dwelling should be kept inviolate as your personal domain.

BLESSED BE THIS DOOR

When several people live under one roof, no matter how harmonious their natures may be, or how many interests, traits, and tastes they may have in common, they still need individual privacy at times. For instance, picture a happy family together, with older brother energetically playing the piano, mother noisily washing the dishes, younger brother practicing jazz on the saxophone, one sister doing high-school homework, another listening to a horror story on the radio, and father watching wrestling on television—all in the ultramodern doorless apartment or ranch house, with the rooms separated from each other by nothing more than plastic curtains. In such an atmosphere, can each of them find individual relaxation? Conceivably; but the odds are against it.

Of course, the nostalgic memory of such an *enforced* family union lasts a lifetime. If some member of that intimate family becomes a writer, he will have plenty of first-hand material for producing a best-seller dealing with an odd mixture of pathos, comedy, and nervous breakdowns. But this compulsory and emotionally stifling sense of mass living can be eliminated and family ties can be strengthened if each adult member is given more privacy.

For example, the father may be physically tired and therefore would probably benefit most by complete repose in an easy chair while listening to soft music or a similar mild entertainment. The mother may find relaxation in watching her favorite TV show. The daughter conceivably could relax best from her school homework by watching a kitten playing with a ball of twine. The nine-year-old boy can relax by active toymaking. Is it reasonable to expect all this to go on simultaneously in one practically doorless apartment or modern house?

Nowadays in the small house or apartment dwelling, the type of interior architecture which inappropriately substitutes curtains or archways for doors robs the individual of his precious solitude. Such beautiful but unrealistic designing can be a cause for much friction. The archway saves the builder money at the expense of the tenant's nerves. This is the worst kind of false economy.

Cubbyholes and confined living spaces are here to stay; but at least let's give the individual privacy when he wants it. Ideally, each member of the family should have his own private room, however small, in which he can find inner peace and quiet. "I want to be alone" is more than a figure of speech. For a cherished period of solitude the private room with a door becomes a necessity. The door locks out would-be intruders and it locks in the occupant of the room. An appropriate sign over every such barrier could be:

> *Blessed be this door.* May it be sturdy and sound-proof, and give me the privacy that I'm entitled to. May it also give my loved ones the opportunity to acquire the tranquillity and peace of not having me around for a while!

CONQUERING NOISE

Noise can destroy our peace of mind and sense of humor, shatter our nerves, interfere with the proper functioning of our body, and rob us of good will and emotional control. Of course, we cannot banish noise. It is an unavoidable part of living. But for the purposes of relaxation we should reduce it as much as possible. A good starting point is with ourselves.

Let us cultivate the habit of the soft-spoken voice. Speaking softly is not only easy on the speaker, but also on the person spoken to. Do you wish to influence others? Then say what you have to say in low tones and choose your words carefully. If the tone and quality of your voice are "just right," no one is likely to find you overbearing no matter *what* you say.

Another frequent source of noise comes from the mechanical contraptions of neighbors living over us, under us, or alongside of us. This source of irritation cannot be fully overcome by modern apartment cave dwellers. Complete soundproofing is ultraexpensive. But if we *mentally minimize* the significance of the noise, it has less effect on us physically. This same attitude of making the best of things reduces the effect of other bothersome intrusions in our environment. When we cannot remove petty irritations, we should try to ignore them.

Unfortunately we are usually less tolerant of noises stemming from members of our own household. Nonetheless, we should try to take the same charitable attitude toward family noises that we take toward those of the neighborhood.

Obviously then you must expect unavoidable sound and relax to its impact. As in falling on the hard ground, the blow hurts less when you "let yourself go." If noises become too distressing, and you can't close your mind to them, or walk away, try ear plugs or anything else which may afford you temporary relief. Yet ultimately, you must look for quietude, as you do for happiness, *within yourself*—it cannot be found anywhere else!

18.

The Family

FATHER, RELAX! · ONLY A HOUSEWIFE?
BRINGING UP GRANDPA

THE most important thing in life for most human beings is marriage and all that it implies—home, children, a joyful sense of roots and security. Unfortunately, we adults are only rarely trained or instructed for this all-important partnership. When courses in mental hygiene and preparation for marriage are offered in every high school, they will help to diminish the number of broken homes and nervous breakdowns that follow in the wake of ignorance, immaturity, unnecessary disappointments, and gross misunderstanding.

To every marriage the wife and the husband each brings a different philosophy of living and a different goal, but at first these differences are overshadowed by the deeper and stronger emotion of love. Most of the time, though, we are unprepared for the sacrifices we must make if the marriage is to be a success. Fortunately, these sacrifices seem unimportant compared to the more dominant need to "belong" and to secure protection and love from each other.

It is well to remember that in all family relationships co-operation yields the best by-products. We should never act so as to make our husband or wife feel weak, dependent—or too important either! Except in an emergency, domestic undertakings should be performed for the good of the whole group and not just to please or "save" someone else.

In the relaxed home, cheerful performance of our normal duties will give us pleasure. By doing these things whole-heartedly, we leave no loophole for feelings of resentment.

When we want to influence others in the family circle, it is well to remember that the most effective way to do so is by setting a more mature example of conduct. While it is difficult to influence anyone, especially where there is hidden resistance, at least you will have the satisfaction of knowing that you are trying your best. But be sure that your physical-mental health does not suffer in the process. Hold to the thought that, "If people or things can't be *changed for the better,* I will certainly not worsen the situation by letting myself become resentful or frustrated."

You cannot expect your personal life to be free from troubles. There are even many social and environmental irritations from which you should not attempt to escape, because they are in reality *strengthening influences.* Brush aside familiar annoyances as you do sweat from your brow or dust from your clothes. A good measure of manageable trouble is always a part of zestful living. Your character is strengthened when you face problems with the feeling that you have the power to overcome them.

Emotional control, especially in relation to your loved ones with whom you live on terms of intimacy, is a necessity. But do not achieve it at the expense of your heart, stomach, or other vital parts of the body. When you become wrought up, walk off your emotion, chop wood, wash windows, or find some useful physical *outlet* for your tension.

It is far better to clear the air by occasionally "blowing off steam" than to keep accumulated resentments and frustrations bottled up within you, for this merely prolongs group tension and irritability.

You can improve your relaxation when you understand yourself as well as those with whom you live. Recognize that it is natural for you to have *mixed* feelings of like and dislike, love and hate toward members of your own household. An understanding of this dual emotional impulse will help to lower your normal resentment against yourself when your behavior is inappropriate. Thus it will lessen your self-blame if, in a moment of annoyance, you have fiercely reprimanded your child; or if, in another moment of excessive affection, you have unwisely acquiesced to some foolish demand.

Our emotions are continually in a state of flux. No one is *always* lovable or agreeable, nor are we so consistent as to always hate or be contrary (fortunately!). Be at peace with yourself. Thank Providence for having given you a sense of proportion and a sense of humor—and keep cultivating both these saving graces.

Be realistic. Where there is much love, at times there is bound to be its counterpart. If you lived continuously in perfect peace, you would soon cease to appreciate it. Therefore, neither you nor your family should consider yourselves neurotic just because emotional flare-ups develop from time to time.

Common "garden varieties" of family tensions are often best checked by short periods of rest. The following are hints on relaxation for various members of the family.

FATHER, RELAX!

The modern father is usually aware of his social responsibilities in the upbringing of his child and looks upon such duties as necessary and agreeable. He is even ready to forfeit some of his own vanishing freedoms in the process. But when he fails to throw off the strain of the working day, he is ill-prepared to deal with his offspring.

Where the father takes the time to relax, and trains himself in patiently guiding the child's behavior, he is more likely to draw the youngster closer to him. He will not be alarmed when some of his own dubious characteristics are apparent in his progeny, and he will derive great joy in cultivating the affection and obedience of his child. However, he should not permit himself to "spoil" the child by countermanding reasonable requests made by the mother —or other adults—or by bestowing upon his son or daughter exceptional favors in order to gain the child's affection. Any hint of favoritism carries with it doubtful benefits to the parent and dangers for the child.

On the other hand, the tense father who looks upon the legitimate requests of the child as a nuisance later has many years of bitter regret. When he finally wakes up to the fact that he has lost the soul-satisfying contact with his child, it may be too late to cement the broken ties. Or when he asserts his *nerve-tensioned authority*, as he often does, by unreasonably scolding or punishing the child, abusing or rejecting him, he may be unwittingly preparing his youngster for the role of juvenile delinquent.

"We are a bundle of habits," according to the great psychologist, William James. Take full advantage of this biological fact in all your relationships with your child, and let this principle *work for you instead of against you*. The precious dividends of a close association between father and child can last a lifetime. But unfortunately if some form of friendly and affectionate understanding isn't established early enough, lonesomeness and remorse may be our lot in the years to come.

In his home many a weary father acts like a bull in a china shop, then later condemns himself for his behavior. When a man returns to his family at night, he should not let the jarring tensions and haste of his business day enter the house with him.

In the home, we should not expect things to run as smoothly as in the shop or the office. Living by precision is a man-made or artificial way of life. Clocks are made by man. Working on strict time schedules, and motoring on crowded roads compels us to abide by demanding man-made rules. This is all the more reason why you should guard against bringing into the home the tension that you are living and working under during the day.

Establish the "reflex" habit of completely relaxing for ten to fifteen minutes upon entering your home. Throwing off the irritations of the day will help you to minimize the occasional irritations of family living. The food may even taste better, and the meal will certainly digest better. Familiar trials and tribulations can be aired later in the evening.

So take it easy. Suppose things are not in their exact place, or your wife and children don't jump to attention as you enter; dinner isn't ready, or a dish isn't to your liking; or you miss a favorite radio or TV program? So what? Remind yourself of the really basic values. And see to it that you really act like the kind and considerate father you picture yourself to be.

As you turn the key in the door of your home, turn on a smile. If you meet signs of discord, make yourself relax; and say nothing that reveals you are aware of the troubled atmosphere. If family storms have been brewing, give them every opportunity to quiet down. Often we can minimize a threatened outburst of dissension by ignoring it.

ONLY A HOUSEWIFE?

Of course, the housewife's lot is not an easy one, but she can find many ways to relax from home duties. Unnecessary fatigue sets in while doing housework when a woman makes a habit of using more energy than the job requires. At the first clear sign of fatigue, you should change to another task. If fatigue continues, exercise that part of the body which you have been using. If your fingers, arms, or shoulders ache, exercise, shake, and wriggle them; also stretch and exercise your neck muscles a bit. If you have been sitting too long or maintaining one position for too long a time, rotate your body from side to side; bend forward and back for a minute or two. If you have been standing too long, stretch your lower back and leg muscles; wriggle and shake your legs. Then take a ten- or fifteen-minute rest period. You will find that you return to your work with a zest that will more than compensate for the time lost by the clock.

Conserve your energy by sitting, standing, walking, and working in the prescribed relaxed position (see chapter 6). Some of the chores you usually perform standing, you can do as well if not better in a sitting position. The use of a tall stool in the kitchen is a great energy saver and should be more frequently employed than it is. Smile instead of frowning; the effect on your work will be astonishing.

In cleaning, stand erect, or bend at the hips instead of high at the waist. In *lifting*, let your body act as a co-ordinated unit by using the larger and stronger leg muscles instead of the smaller ones of the arms and back. When ironing, make sure that the ironing board is the right height for you, so that you will not tire your back. Many a housewife has found that all her tasks become easier when performed to the rhythm of music.

WRONG　　　　　　RIGHT

WRONG　　　　　　RIGHT

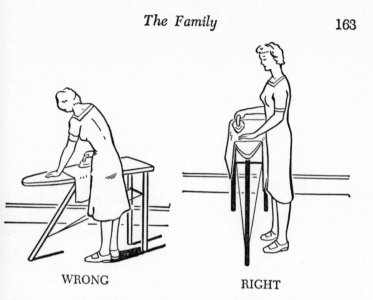

WRONG RIGHT

If you want to feel at ease, do not imagine yourself to be perfect, or work too hard to make just *one* thing perfect. Otherwise, you may overlook *other* and more important things, such as approaching "deadlines" for different tasks. And when you become aware that "time has run out," you are bound to become tense. So if you feel overwhelmed by the many tasks still ahead of you, form the habit of choosing what is most important in your list of "priorities." Never try to have everything sparklingly clean and tidy at the expense of the happiness and tranquillity of your family.

One way to *lessen the tension and confusion* of your daily life is to list all your activities planned for one day. Put on this list only the tasks that you may reasonably be able to complete today, not things to do tomorrow, or next week, or next month. Let your schedule be flexible. Preserve a hopeful attitude toward all tasks left undone. Allow yourself plenty of extra margin for normal inefficiency and unexpected delays.

As you are doing your work, have a pencil and paper handy. When a task enters your mind, add it to your list. At the end of the day, you will know exactly what you didn't do. But you will also know what you *did* do. You may be surprised by how many varied tasks you have performed. Instead of trying to "get everything done" in short order, appreciate yourself for the things you have already accomplished. Big problems seem smaller when sliced into a series of smaller ones. And be sure to place on your list this starred memo: *"Relax for ten minutes every hour!"*

Be prepared mentally to take in your stride any deviation from the usual routine. When you are expecting visitors, for instance, do not make them a legitimate excuse to become thoroughly exhausted by the time they appear. Relax a bit before your friends arrive. Do not hesitate—if necessary—to go into your bedroom, close the door, and find some temporary but complete repose. Then you will enjoy your friends in a relaxed manner and voice and with a pleasant expression on your face.

Tension and nervousness often make even the more agreeable aspects of homemaking seem drudgery. When you are tired, it is easy to forget that your job requires creative ability—that it means something more than merely having children or being a housekeeper or a scrubwoman.

Yours is the opportunity to make your home a pleasant, kindly, serene haven for your loved ones, a citadel to which they can retreat with confidence and safety. And what a lift you can give your despondent or depressed husband and "defeated" child when they come in from the harsher outer world! Speak to them in a soft agreeable voice. Choose the *right* time to speak. Then your words will not make your listeners feel weak or resentful. And *don't nibble at your husband's ego.* The wife's job is to *build him up*—and keep him there.

BRINGING UP GRANDPA

Is a grandparent a problem in your home? If so, how are you coping with this age-old conflict between the generations? Do you depend excessively upon your parents? Do you fail to recognize their lowered general health, their increased crotchetiness, and their lessened emotional ability to take noise, or to witness the hyper-active goings-on of the children in your family?

Or, are you inclined to look upon these grandparents as a nuisance and a source of irritation because their point of view is so different from yours? When young people do not occasionally place themselves in the older generation's shoes, they often hurt them to the very core by showing disrespect for their personalities and way of doing things. So don't weaken their morale by needless callousness unless you want to take the very heart out of them. And remember your parents love you dearly and are trying their best to help you make your house a home.

It generally pleases older people to discuss freely and often small everyday problems with you, for this makes them feel that you still consider them to be socially useful and in full possession of their faculties. But it is wiser not to tell your parents your major troubles and worries because they can no longer be of any concrete help to you in solving them. Above all, use your imagination! Try to see their point of view.

19.

Tensions Transferred

RELAXED MOTHER—RELAXED CHILD

TENSIONS and irritations are contagious—they spread from the parent to the child. The child puts up his defenses by either withdrawing or reacting violently and in either case shuts out his parent from his inner mental life.

The wise mother allows herself time to talk and to listen. She establishes the positive habit of relaxing, forgetting her petty troubles by wholeheartedly playing with her child. When she laughs with him at his games, reads his books to him, uses his crayon pencils, brushes, and other devices or toys, she lays the foundation for a lifelong feeling of affection and intimacy. There is no better path to a healthy child-parent relationship.

All the books on psychology are wasted unless the mother has learned to apply psychology to herself. Don't be one of the "young-fashioned" mothers who, irritated by the child's insistent interference with her reading of the latest child psychology book, flies off the handle and uses the volume in an old-fashioned way on that part of the child's anatomy "where it will do the most good." Should you decide to spank your youngster, be sure to explain to him why you punished him in this manner. Some psychologists agree with the "Quiz Kids"—that it's better to *explain before* the spanking is given. When the episode is over, forget that it "hurt you more than it did him," don't be resentful that he "made you do it," and show the child that you love him just the same.

Of course, you should make doubly sure that your disciplinary action is not a result of irritations traceable to someone else in the family, your husband perhaps, or your mother-in-law. Don't penalize your child because you are annoyed that your next-door neighbor bought the same hat!

Watch and listen as your child plays with other children, especially when the girls "play house." Furnish them with plenty of dolls—a mama, papa, baby, and even grandma doll! If you can't afford to buy such distinctive dolls, dress up your child's old dolls to resemble in some way these familiar family characters. Then observe carefully how she plays with them, how she talks to them, and what they are made to do to or with each other.

Don't be shocked when you notice your children caricaturing or mimicking the other members of your family. Does your little daughter kick the baby doll, or talk to the father doll in the tone that you employ to your husband? If you listen carefully, *you can hear yourself as your child hears you,* and discover in this way valuable information about some of your own worthy or unworthy behavior.

BEWARE OF YOUR EMOTIONS

When it is necessary to punish your child, *never do it in anger* for you only pass on your tension to the child and arouse a corresponding hostility in him. The relaxed parent does not concentrate the child's attention on his "bad" habits. He presents him instead with a number of alternatives differing in degrees of merit. This may help distract the child's attention from his less desirable habits. An excessive and continuous dosage of "don'ts" serves chiefly to focus a child's mind on what he should *not* do, but supplies him with no clear or attractive options.

For example, instead of harshly scolding or reprimanding the young child for nervously biting his nails or sucking his thumb—which is usually a compensating habit for some kind of rejection—show him more kindness and affection. Nighttime fear or lonesomeness can be reduced by keeping a faint subdued light in his room, or by giving him a Teddy bear or a doll to hold as he falls asleep.

Other responses, such as childhood masturbation, are soon overcome if the child's attention is not sharply drawn in that direction through punishment, and if no undue issue is made of this innocent and universally prevalent *passing* habit of childhood. The chief danger in many cases is overemphasis and excessive anger on the part of a disturbed parent.

The first psychological casualty of ordinary weariness and tension is the mother's loss of patience and good judgment. You expect the impossible; you look for unwarranted sympathy. You wonder why your loved ones are so unreasonable in their demands, and why they are not moderately considerate of you. You become annoyed with everybody and everything, even yourself. So it's little wonder that this mood transfers itself to your small child.

For instance, you put the child to bed and heave a sigh of relief. You expect him or her to fall asleep immediately. The thought in your mind is, "Now I will be able to do my necessary chores" or breathe more freely for a few minutes. But a child isn't so considerate. He frequently struggles against going to sleep. You become annoyed. His nightly dozen "innocent" little requests at bedtime quickly shatter your remaining composure. You reinforce with harshness your demands for the sandman to come quickly. Finally, with a grim feeling of parental rejection, your child cries himself to sleep, and you close his door with an ugly feeling of guilt. This picture is repeated in countless households every night.

How can you put the child to sleep, and yet find a measure of relaxation at the same time? Anticipate first his strong antipathy to being separated from the family circle. Recall your own feelings when you were a child, when the demand "go to sleep" was a sentence of banishment.

How can you take the cutting edge off this daily child-adult separation? In general, by eliminating the spirit of mutual combat. By gentle firmness, lead the youngster to bed. Avoid any show of anger at his violent protests or tantrums. As he quiets down, demonstrate your continuing affection for him. Read him a story, hum a tune. Teach him quietude as you teach yourself patience. Sit beside him. Enjoy some of this enforced leisure. Your child should then fall asleep with diminished resentment and with much greater affection for you.

The time spent in putting your child to sleep can either wreck your nerves, or relax them. If you anticipate your child's questions and his myriad requests, you will not be upset. And when he finally falls asleep, you too will be rested.

Other considerations: The mother's *anxiety* can be fully

as damaging to her child as her anger. When a child is sick, for instance, it is an old adage among doctors that *a tense mother means a sicker child.* Too many parents permit panic to shine through their eyes. They become unduly alarmed, wear stark anxiety on their countenances, and show it in their postures. This exaggeration of a normal pattern undoubtedly worsens the child's illness if for no other reason than that the parents' fear is transferred to the child. Too much attention or overurgent feeding will make your child conscious of his parents' anxiety.

Even if your child is delicate, do not force him into a hothouse existence. You may feel, sadly enough, that "life is so cruel," and that heavy responsibilities will come to the youngster soon enough, so he should have his fun while he can. Unfortunately, instead of strengthening the child's personality, this attitude tends to soften his moral fiber and diminish his chances of living effectively in the hard world of reality.

A less worthy reason for overindulging a child is one parent's desire to win the child's affection from the other. And the child is quick either to detect or make unworthy use of love when it is a cunning form of bribery.

Too often the unconscious motives of the parent who wants to give the child everything are not founded upon wisdom or necessity, but are the fulfillment of a selfish ego-satisfying desire to give the child everything that the parent didn't have in his own childhood. Then the fathers and mothers hope to be repaid by the child in their later years. They overlook the fact that, when the child is softened and weakened by too much attention, he becomes not only incapable of finding happiness and usefulness for himself, but that he has a lessened capacity to be grateful to his parents.

Even the wisest parents are sometimes overwhelmed

with guilt when they see unfortunate tendencies developing in their offspring. But it is well to remember that yours are not the only influences that are molding his personality. You cannot discount the influence of other children, as well as his aunts, uncles, and grandparents. The behavior of every stranger has its full impact upon the child. Advertisements, current journalism and literature, the voices and pictures coming over the air through radio and TV, and the comics—all these influences too help to shape his character and outlook.

But this is only the beginning of the social elements at work. The child's schoolteachers, fellow classmates, and casual acquaintances complicate the development of his personality. On the physiological side, his glandular make-up, organ inferiorities, nerve irritations, and hereditary characteristics are basic influences.

When one considers all these factors, why should you— or any parent—feel *totally* responsible for your child's behavior? The best any parent can do is to give the child a comfortable home, a full measure of love and understanding (which includes obligations as well as privileges), and set the best possible examples for happy family living.

COPING WITH THE ADOLESCENT

The teen-age son or daughter is a disconcerting new source of family tensions. The parent, bewildered and irritated almost beyond endurance by the adolescent's unpredictable behavior, is likely to fall back on his habit of authority. But the "do's" and "don't's" that exacted unquestioning obedience no longer are effective. And so the tension grows.

The parents' hopeful attitude of "I understand you, because I too was young once" may have held true formerly but it does not in the mid-twentieth century. Adolescents today face new problems that were absent in past generations. They are also subject to fresh and powerful morale-shattering influences, and to a lamentable lack of those useful and responsible tasks which either came naturally to, or were forced upon, the youth of a half-century ago. Consequently, youngsters are now not only harder to understand but also more difficult to "manage."

It may help to realize that the adolescent is biologically an adult. He is able to wear adult clothes and to drive an automobile. He has the capacity to fulfill all his basic needs. He can hear, read, and see almost the entire range of human experience, dramatized through all channels of public information, temptingly exaggerated by experts in the art of salesmanship. All the world's luxuries, allure, and excitement are dangled before his gaze. Sex is brilliantly glorified through every medium of publicity. Yet parents, as well as teachers, clergy, the government, and the unwritten laws of our necessary moral code, constantly proclaim, "You mustn't! You're not old enough! You haven't a job!" The real wonder is that juvenile delinquency is not more prevalent, considering all the factors that tend to increase it.

When parents reflect upon the emotional and biological storms that often rage within the adolescent, the temptations to which he is subject, the acute loneliness and yearning which occasionally possess him, and his frequent spells of sheer emptiness and despair, they may be less disturbed by sudden outbursts of adolescent temper. The parent who is free from strain himself will realize that youth is merely expressing its rebellion before the persons with whom he feels most free, and at home, where he feels relatively at ease.

In dealing with their teen-age children, relaxed parents rely upon their intuitive sense, and upon the promptings of love and understanding. They give the adolescent every opportunity to assume his just responsibilities, to deal co-operatively with the family's problems, and to make his contribution democratically by free expression of his views and ideas. Wise parents harness their patience under pressure and wait for the teen-ager's mood of revolt to change.

And then remember that the normal adolescent, although far from genuinely neurotic, often reacts like a neurotic to the new vibrant changes going on within him, largely because he feels torn between antagonistic forces. He may want to have his cake and eat it at the same time. While he sorely needs the protection and affection of his parents, he also bitterly resents it, because he wants to be completely on his own. He easily becomes frustrated because he cannot do what he wants.

Wise parents know that this internal confusion of values and purposes will make for discord, and they are glad that it finds a safe outlet in the home. The clashing emotions of like and dislike for his parents are anticipated, and accepted as an unavoidable phenomenon.

HOW TO STUDY

Parents are often irritated by the awkward way their high-school and even college sons and daughters sit when they study. Body contortions are usually signs of tension, and wise parents will attempt to find what is generating it. Perhaps the parents themselves are at fault. Even though in some extreme cases tensions may have a long head start, the efforts to understand them are well worth while. Here are some of the more usual causes of teen-age tension.

1. Too heavy a school schedule.
2. Pressure of parental expectation. For example, "You must get a grade of Excellent." "You must stand high in your class."

3. Taunts of fellow pupils.

4. Poor relations with one or more teachers.

5. Overanxiety, fear, worry, depression, self-consciousness or feelings of inferiority which tie the pupil up in mental or physical knots.

6. Poor health (malnutrition, bad posture, etc.).

7. Overprotection.

8. Adverse home influences.

9. Inner emotional conflicts.

When you have done your best to eliminate the causes of the tension, remind your child that there is a technique of studying, an efficient and an inefficient way. Here are a few tips that will show your youngsters how to work in an easy relaxed manner.

The student can avoid the fatigue of sustained reading or writing, work longer, and feel more alert if he sits up erect. If he sits in a deep chair, and leans back too far, he may become too relaxed and so hamper concentration. Therefore the student's chair should be exactly the right height for him so that the entire weight of his feet and legs can rest firmly on the floor.

The youngster should avoid such common errors of posture as crossing his legs, sitting in a contorted position, or tilting his head. When reading or listening, he shouldn't cross his arms over his chest as that interferes with proper breathing. His arms and hands should rest on his desk or table, or on his thighs. His head is poised or evenly balanced on his neck. Shoulders are not raised or twisted.

Check the way your child holds a pen or pencil. Much depends on whether he grips it tightly or holds it lightly. He should write softly, use a pencil with a frictionless point, or a smooth-flowing pen. He should make well-formed letters, and occasionally shift the paper surface as well as the pencil.

The student's facial muscles should be relaxed. While his mind must be active, his forehead need not be furrowed! His jaw should not become set, his teeth should not grit, or his eyes squint. He won't increase his receptivity by scowling at the paper, tensing his whole body, stiffening his shoulders, and biting or sticking out his tongue like a small child. A confident and faintly smiling facial expression is an asset to relaxation.

A few minutes of *slow-double-stretching* of his muscles can make your child fully relaxed, and serve the dual purpose of awakening his creative impulses and quickening his mental processes. During this *brief* pause he should close his eyes and mentally take himself to the most distant and enchanted land. He should place himself in the midst of beautiful and fantastic scenes. But he must retain a full awareness of the reserves of strength and endurance within him. Your child must have confidence in his abilities.

The student should not let interruptions bother him. Sometimes they cannot be ignored but the teen ager can learn to build a "mental fence" around himself. And if these distractions cannot be removed or remedied, he must learn to relax to them. The person who is "keen" on his work and recognizes its importance is scarcely aware of the annoyances around him. Even slight illnesses or physical pains worry him scarcely at all.

Contrary to common thinking and practice, *intense* concentration is not a requisite for good learning. Nervous tension plus desperate concentration often defeats creativeness. While a child necessarily generates *a certain amount of specific tension in learning anything,* by lessening the *general* tension he reduces the total energy required for study and heightens the efficiency of his learning process. But to become overanxious, to attempt to do too much, or to concentrate too furiously serves only to defeat his purpose. The toxins generated in the brain from mental fatigue linger on. The harder a teen ager studies under stress, the more he wears himself out, and the longer it takes him to grasp the subject. Hence, the necessity to break frequently, even for a few minutes, spells of tension and anxiety. Then the child can go back to his studying with renewed vigor.

Teach your children to *trust their brains.* The human mind is far more efficient than a tape recorder. It has a tremendous capacity to register and store impressions of all kinds. All that a person has learned is filed away in his brain as memory traces. How else could anyone recall happenings or material learned years ago? So even a hasty review will usually bring back and revive much of the material already studied.

When a person's brain is functioning properly, it plays back what was recorded. Anxiety and haste are the common gremlins that hamper a student's mental "playback." But there is no doubt that he can heighten the ratio of retention and increase his powers of recall when he is eager to retain what he has studied, preserves a hopeful frame of mind, keeps in good health and does his studying under the best possible conditions.

One of the easiest ways for a student to tap his unconscious mind for the material that he wants to remember is to become completely passive. This method has been adapted successfully to commercial use by the Dormiphone Company that makes records for studying languages. While the student is drowsily falling asleep, the Dormiphone record keeps on playing, and thus teaches the average pupil much faster than the usual way.

No one should go to bed while his mind is still alert and active. Try taking some moderate physical exercise or a hot bath. Or, better still, use the relaxation method prescribed. Then go to sleep with the thought in your mind that the material you have been studying will "come through." You are likely to wake up with that same thought in the morning, and find that your subconscious has been working for you.

Obviously all this advice to teen-age students is equally applicable to white-collar workers who are chained to a desk for long hours at a time.

20.

Aids for Advancing Years

RESET YOUR RHYTHMOSTAT

WITH advancing years comes the time to reset your rhythmostat at a lower point of activity. Your spirit may be as young as ever but for your health's sake slow down. After middle age exercise is a dangerous luxury, especially if you have been inactive in late years. The heart won't take the punishment it once did, so admit your age to yourself and act accordingly. Learn to chuckle a bit about the things you want to do but cannot—or should not.

When you are advancing in years you should heed fatigue, for it is one of the beneficent warnings that nature gives us. Many wise older people recognize this instinctively and stop their activities before they are exhausted. As soon as they begin to feel tired or their eyes become strained, they must rest a while. When they are reading or watching television, for instance, they ease the tension by taking a couple of deep breaths or stretching now and then. A good rule is to close the eyes during the commercials!

If you are on the farther side of fifty most of the suggestions for relaxation in the preceding chapters will be particularly valuable to you. Be patient and cautious while learning to use them, and you will find them especially helpful in preserving your health and ease of mind.

WHEN TO RETIRE

When should you retire? There is no definite rule—at sixty or after or before, depending upon your state of health and your plans for the future. But whenever you do it, make up your mind to accept retirement gracefully.

The adjustment will not be easy. You will find yourself facing many new problems, among them what to do with your time and how to adjust your social life. Then too, you know that with advancing years your susceptibility to illness may increase. Furthermore, when you are freed from the rush and strain of a busy active life, it is well to remember not to utilize your extra time in worrying or fretting.

Unfortunately the sudden retirement that most of us face is out of step with everything in nature. Nothing in the natural order of things comes on suddenly. We are not born suddenly, we seldom die suddenly. Therefore we should not retire with a sudden wrench from the busy life that we have known for so many years. It shakes our morale. It is a strain on the rhythm of our body and mind, because we crave not only rest, but also a certain amount of activity.

Sudden and complete retirement is not only nonsensical but hazardous to mental and physical health. Our muscles are like engines, and when they suddenly fall into disuse, they "rust" and lose their power. Consequently, the probability of physical illness is increased. It is heightened by overeating. Our eating habits have become so ingrained that we don't decrease the amount of food we eat to match our decreased activity. Indeed, we may even eat more because we have fewer things to do! The extra pounds strain the heart, kidneys, and other vital organs, and hasten most of the diseases of old age.

Purposeless leisure also gives us more time to be bored and to harbor unhappy thoughts—remorse about the past and misgivings about the future. When our thoughts are no longer centered about our work, they concentrate more and more upon ourselves. When we allow ourselves to brood we become increasingly conscious of our minor pains and aches.

Thus the retirement which we anticipated with pleasure can turn out to be a menace to our well-being. Partial retirement, on the other hand, can be a blessing. It permits us to slow down. We have more time to enjoy things, yet we do not feel that we have been "put on the shelf." So if it is at all practicable, see that you retire in *easy steps*.

If your work does not permit you to do this, then jump into some other occupation in which you can still utilize your mental and physical energies. Do not permit yourself to freeze into inactivity.

It is natural for discouragement to set in occasionally. The cure for it is to accept cheerfully and with confidence, situations that can not be changed. And above all, work at something—at a slower pace in keeping with your age. Activity is the secret of enjoying prolonged leisure.

START SOMETHING NEW

Why not make retirement an opportunity to start something new? It is amazing how quickly you will discover talents that you never knew you had. Your hands, for instance, are incredible. Your fingertips contain more than one and a half million nerve-sense organs. When you begin to use your hands creatively you will find new ideas for utilizing those materials within your reach. Even deformed hands can do amazing things.

Do not be afraid of new adventures. When you get an idea, you may think "I cannot do that; I'm too old." But hold onto the idea. Go to the library and read all the literature you can find on the subject. What a satisfaction you will experience when you do something that neither you nor anyone else thought possible. You may not write a prize-winning best seller, or receive an award for sculpture, or have your song set to music and played in every jukebox, but you will get an unexpected amount of pleasure out of accomplishing something that you did not believe you could.

If you have the desire to be useful, there is an infinite variety of things that will suggest themselves. Encourage yourself to develop interests for which you had little time before you retired.

Perhaps you always had an inclination to help the sick. Why not revive it? One spry old gentleman of seventy-three finds short-term jobs for himself by placing occasional small ads in the local paper, offering to nurse nervous patients. He receives more replies than he can answer. By following the instructions of the doctor or psychiatrist in charge of the case, he helps to make it unnecessary for the patient to be confined in a mental institution. So when this old man is occupied he forgets his loneliness and takes satisfaction in the knowledge that there is still a valuable niche in life for him.

Your services will also be welcomed as a hospital volunteer. There you can more or less choose your own time, and do as much or as little as you like. The Red Cross offers you an opportunity to do part-time volunteer work, and so does your church.

Or you may not want to go so far afield. By looking around, you may find something to do in your own neighborhood, even at your own doorstep. One vigorous grandmother did just this. She is seventy-eight. Her seven children have all married and moved away, leaving her desperately lonely, so she keeps herself busy by baby-sitting for mothers in her apartment house. For her the days no longer drag. She is not living on borrowed time.

Lonesomeness is one of the greatest curses of old age. One way to overcome it is to *talk* to people. Don't be taken aback if you meet with a rebuff. Other people are lonely too and most of the time they will welcome making conversation.

And why not be active in some group welfare undertaking, especially if the family has dwindled or family relationships have become strained? We all have a great need of belonging and we need to be doing something for our fellow men. Sitting around and merely *watching* people doing things gives you the feeling that life has passed you by.

GLOOM CHASERS

There are many things that you can do to chase away your gloom. Even secretly learning to play the harmonica may give you a lot of fun. Surprise a youngster by making a toy for him. Discover the birthdays of some of your friends and send them cards. Write a letter to your newspaper—it's a thrill to see your name in print. Revive one of your childhood hobbies. Visit a friend. Surprise the bus driver by giving him a cheery "hello." Find something to laugh about, or at least to evoke a smile. Start the day with zest, with hope and with plans. It is much better to plan too many things and then be unconcerned about how much you accomplish than to drag through the day with nothing much to do.

When you feel gloom descending, you may get a lift by wearing something colorful—a bright tie or a bright-colored dress or hat, or changing to a new suit. Incidentally, clothes and jewelry are always a good topic of conversation, particularly when your friend or neighbor starts to tell you the story of an old and well-knitted surgical operation.

Another rule for contentment is to participate in the activities of the young—not so much from the point of view of teaching them, although that too is a joy, but rather by permitting them to teach you. When you enter the life of the young, time temporarily stands still.

Enter into the hearts of your grandchildren by easy stages. Let them set the pace for your companionship. Ask a question or two about their present interest; then keep still. They will come to you. Subdue your eagerness, and wait until you are invited to work at their projects with their friends. Tell them stories or play with their toys. During the play you may sandwich in a nugget or two of wisdom which they will later digest. But be careful that your nuggets contain no "do's" or "don'ts"!

The young cannot readily enter into your world, nor should you permit yourself to unburden all your woes upon them. But it pleases them when you listen to _their_ problems and ideas and it saves _you_ from living in the _past_.

AFTER THE DOCTOR LEAVES

Although your mind may be as alert as ever, you cannot escape the fact that your body is aging. There is nothing you can do to stop the changes that are going on but you can assume a mature attitude toward your health. A cheerful state of mind helps to lessen the inevitable aches and pains. Do not permit them to stop your everyday activities. Slow down—yes—but do not give in to your distress unless the cure depends upon a complete temporary cessation of activity.

There are two positive things that you can, and indeed, should do.

1. Obtain professional help to discover the nature or cause of your ailment.

2. Follow your doctor's advice but do not feel that your recovery is entirely his business and that you yourself need do nothing about it. Health cannot be bought like a hat or a pair of shoes. Usually you can do much to either hinder or hasten your recovery. No matter how conscientious your doctor is, he cannot possibly find the time to advise you in detail how to relax or to give you other explicit directions for your daily well-being. The suggestions in this volume will most likely supplement his treatments. Relaxation, *when performed cautiously,* will always aid in your recovery.

In the old days our grandfathers obtained relief from ordinary aches and pains by the use of simple remedies. They wore a nightcap as a protection against the cold and used snuff to clear the nasal passages. Diluted apple-cider vinegar was used as a gargle and for many other purposes, such as head and stomach aches. (It is still a standard remedy in many parts of Vermont.) Herbs were used extensively. On cold nights our ancestors slept on a blanket for added warmth and wore socks to keep their feet warm. Peppermint tea was a heating drink. Crude as these and many other simple remedial measures were, they gave our grandparents relief and sleep and eased their minor pains.

Nowadays, when professional help is easily available, it is wiser to stop guessing about your ailments or doctoring yourself. A physical examination may free you from your worries or you may be better able to adjust yourself to your physical difficulties that cannot be helped. Look upon time as a friend, as a healer and solver of your problems. Let it work for you instead of against you.

HOW ARE YOUR FAMILY RELATIONS?

Since our emotions are to a large extent responsible for our mental and physical state, as well as for our relationships with our sons and daughters, it is well for members of the older generation to examine their behavior. To make sure that we do not become an intolerable burden to our loved ones, we must conduct ourselves with an emotional maturity that matches our physical maturity. *The younger generation, justifiably or not, expects us to have become wise with age,* to know what to do, and especially, what not to do. Inappropriate behavior, such as nagging or faultfinding, is reluctantly tolerated in the old. They are expected to be prudent on all occasions.

Although the young have definite ideas as to how the older generation should behave, we cannot expect them to understand our reasons for discontent. They do not see, for instance, how hard it is to be no longer able to give generously when one had given with a great deal of pride in former years. Nor do they realize that as we grow old our desire for love and affection increases rather than decreases. The only thing we can do about it is to abstain from complaining, as well as from smothering our children with either our fears or our affections and to accept their love when it is given, not as a right, but as a blessing.

DIFFICULTIES OF BEING A GRANDPARENT

It is not easy to be a grandparent, especially for one who lives with his children and has to face the stark reality that he is often in the way. If you are a wise grandparent you will realize that you too must make adjustments. The time is past when you can dominate the family circle.

It is tragic if you have not become wise enough to sever the strangling emotional ties with your children. These perpetuate your children's immaturity. Now that the children are grown, you cannot hope to change them in basic respects; experience will have to do that. Therefore why try to hold onto your former power? It is no longer either necessary or fitting that you should carry the weight of responsibility for your children.

Nor need your esteem suffer when the time comes to accept dependence. Your children probably want to have the satisfaction of caring for you, of repaying you for what you have done for them—if you will only let them, by modifying your faulty behavior. You enjoyed giving; now why not enjoy taking with equal pleasure?

Mellowness and a greater tranquillity should come with advancing years. You will achieve it more easily when you are relaxed and properly nourished, when you have something interesting to occupy your time, when you feel that you are wanted and that there is a need for you. The following are a few of the pitfalls you should try to avoid.

MENTAL HAZARDS OF ADVANCING YEARS

1. Do not blame your children's faults and troubles on yourself. Such a feeling of guilt is useless. There is little you can do now to influence your children's characters or destinies.

2. Be moderate in the giving of your love. Excessive af-

fection leads to self-pity and resentment when you feel that your children are inconsiderate of you. Self-pity pays no dividends. If you allow yourself to sink into that swamp, you continue to be miserable.

3. Don't complain. Complaining is a devastating habit that will go far toward disrupting good family relations. Complain only to those who can or are able to help you. The other alternative is to grin and bear it.

4. Conquer boredom. It can rob you of your zest for living. In addition to work, a good buffer is a sense of humor.

5. Do not demand sympathy. When we ask for it, we reject it as soon as it is given. Instead, let us develop an understanding heart.

21.

Inner Peace

THOUGHTFUL men have learned that God is not only the creator of the unfathomable universe, but also an immediate source of human strength and inspiration. He expresses Himself through the workings and the wisdom of every "truly righteous" human being.

The quotation,

> "I am the place where God shines through,
> For He and I are one, not two,"

is applicable not only to the single individual but to all humanity. Awareness of the presence of that tiny spark of divinity within us gives courage, hope, and strength in health, and in sickness it is often the final thread by which we cling to life.

188

And more strength and power come to us ultimately from those unfathomable forces than from the most nourishing of food. They provide us with greater self-esteem than we could ever get from any outward source of flattery, and more protection than is found in the strongest fortress.

If the body is not too weakened, the forces of life operating through you make every possible attempt to repair and heal the system. Similarly, your aims in life, if not too far-fetched, can be fulfilled; your goals, if not completely out of the realm of possibility, can be reached. While you shouldn't make yourself believe that you are stronger or better than you actually are, it is folly not to rely upon your inexhaustible inner forces. We are profoundly grateful to Him for every degree of ability to enjoy life and to be useful in it. And so, find peace.

SPIRITUAL RELAXATION

Spiritual relaxation often gives us body-mind ease which cannot be obtained by mental or physical relaxation alone. It can reduce our tensions when passions overwhelm us or when we fall into self-pity and remorse.

As a foundation for inner peace and intuitive wisdom, your total organism should first become calm (chapters 4 and 8). As soon as you are properly relaxed, allow yourself to become aware of the strengthening life- and health-giving forces radiating actively through you, and meditate leisurely upon the *larger* aspects of your being.

Once you are spiritually relaxed, you are in a better condition to develop your highest faculties. When confronted with any task, do all you can; then calmly wait a while in silence for guidance as to the next step ahead.

USE OF SPIRITUAL RELAXATION IN SICKNESS

When sickness comes, you normally rely upon the comfort of professional care, your loved ones, and friends; but spiritual relaxation is an important mainstay. During the period of utter repose it confers, all anxiety and fear become subdued or forgotten. Then you won't feel weak, lonesome, or forsaken. Allow yourself to feel safe, even if only temporarily, like an infant under loving and protective parental care.

Here you match your faith against your fears; inner strength against weakness; reserves of basic power to endure and suffer against agonizing pain; courage against failings; resources against lacks. Recall those gratifying or daring experiences through which you have lived. Remember the heroic deeds of others who have conquered sickness and peril. Focus on the truth that, no matter how much is arrayed against you, there is still much unused power residing within you. Do not "suffer in silence." Let down your socially restraining emotional barriers. Allow your best friend, or doctor, to share your somberest thoughts and feelings. Much relief is often found that way.

To be sure, some glorious and wise souls realize the futility of complaining and are shining examples of stoicism. But when everything has been done that apparently can be done, what often turns the tide is the patient's determined reliance upon his own recuperative powers. The possessor of this quality of "will" makes possible God's miracles. How else can we explain some of the astounding recoveries we have seen?

SPIRITUAL STRENGTH

You are an intelligent being. You know how to use the highest faculties of reason and logic. Why then do you succumb to anxiety and doubt? Usually, it is because you fail to use the higher spiritual laws of strength and power operating through you.

Every living creature functions because of those beneficent laws. Man comes into being through creative power, and in turn becomes a generating source of power. Overlook this truth and you feel weak and forsaken. Recognize it, and it makes you strong, removes your tension, and comforts you with a mighty sense of residual power.

You learn to accept the "reality principle" of life—that successes and failures, pain and pleasure, good and bad, sickness and health, are all *part* of complete living. "Fight or flight" is not always the maturest way of coping with reality. Often in facing a hard situation, we must *compromise* with it by being patient and waiting. Through such practical forbearance, we learn how our problems can be more satisfactorily resolved.

Such reality orientation makes you aware that everything within you and about you is in constant change. The human being, an inescapable part of nature, likewise changes. While this is the basis of deterioration, it is also the root of all growth and progress.

The normal practical person seeks to combine realism with spirituality. He does not deny any phase of his physical being, nor the realities of the material world. He illuminates this knowledge and brightens it with the light of inner faith—*faith in himself, faith in his fellow man, and faith in God.* Without this basis for action, none of us could reach success in any sphere of activity.

When depression envelops you, you may ask yourself, "Why are you cast down, oh my soul?" Recall prophetic and comforting words, such as: "Be still; God is with you." Emphasize the spark of divinity within you and your potentialities for joy and health. On the other hand, just as soon as you catch yourself becoming too elated or too "self-important," immediately set yourself on a more even keel by remembering that there are valleys as well as mountain peaks in human experience. This should guard you against becoming obsessed with your own merits or significance.

SPIRITUAL RELATEDNESS

There exists within you an integrating force which fosters your fellowship with the rest of humanity. Full recognition of this fact can eliminate the discomfort of your lonesomeness. You can always depend upon this co-ordinating principle; if properly understood and obeyed, it leads to the free, full, good, creative, and happy life.

The problem of lonesomeness disturbs almost every human being. How can you avoid the intolerable isolation which often comes from the feeling that you stand alone? One of the best means to overcome this solitariness is the conviction that you are intimately connected at all times with the rest of Creation. Whatever you possess and all the joy that you may otherwise experience will have sustaining value only if accompanied by this sense of constant relatedness to some larger Whole.

Accept and affirm joyously the co-ordination and interrelation between people, animals, the earth with all the growing plants, the air, the wind, the stars, and the sun. All these and more are part of one vast plan, of one great cosmos. Every person belongs within this scheme and is a part of it. And a Supreme Intelligent Power rules over all!

There is harmony and rhythm in this entire universe of life and matter. Contemplation of the fact that each of us is a portion of that well-regulated and integrated cosmic whole fills men with awe and worship, heightening their

RESPONSE TO NATURE

Spiritual relaxation is also found in the outdoors. You cannot enjoy the seashore or a walk in the woods without feeling the harmony of Nature.

So whenever you feel tense, worried, fearful, anxious, or when your weakness and failings overwhelm you, visualize Nature's forces, or better yet, go out to watch them. Nature is constantly demonstrating the perennial growth and regenerative power present everywhere and in every human being. Step into the world outside your door at any time of the year and this truth comes home vividly: Spring with its promise, summer with its abundance, autumn with its mature acceptance of inevitably changing patterns, winter with its withdrawal of all "visible" strength but its quiet conservation of the resources required to live and grow again when the cycle of the seasons starts afresh. All the creative forces, nourishing every plant and tree, reside within you as well. Why should you view yourself as less important, in the entire natural scheme of things, than the worst-warped tree or the lowliest plant?

Things may not be running smoothly in your direction right now. But as you stand before a whispering brook, you realize that even obstacles have their good uses. For you can see stones in the brook agitating, and thus purifying the water that runs past them. Similarly, complications that you meet in life may clarify and purify your thoughts and purposes. As blessings in disguise, they lead you to re-evaluate your objectives. Such obstacles dissipate egotism and selfishness, and heighten your determination to go on to solid accomplishment. They force you to realize that you cannot always have "clear sailing," and suggest that there may be sound hidden reasons for delays. When water meets a rock, it does not stop. There may be sound and fury but nevertheless the water rolls on. Life too is a continuous stream of activities and it goes on in spite of all hindrances.

The unyielding force of life is the basic source of strength in man. The mature individual does not permit himself to be stopped in his path by disappointments, sufferings, pains, frustrations, or losses. The law of life simply says, "Go on and on." Follow it; and remember always, *if you can't do everything, you can at least do something.* And so you gain deep personal satisfaction; you pay your debt to contemporary society, to posterity, and ancestry; and thereby win your way to greater spiritual peace.

Within every human soul, there functions the spirit of creativeness. As you become spiritually relaxed, you grow conscious of a private destiny to be fulfilled, and mindful of a power within you for that purpose. This seldom means accomplishments on a grand scale, but it does mean that at least you can make your home more livable, or your club or community a little better. Your "green-thumb" technique with flowers can mean bright bouquets for invalids. Your labors may mean better education for your children, or a good home for the orphaned children of a relative or friend.

And from such helpfulness, you have your answer when you ask yourself the fundamental question, "What is my true value in the scheme of things?" You will be able to answer, "Perhaps I am more useful than I think—I am using my mental and physical energies not only for myself and my family, but my work is benefiting others as well." Or you tell yourself, "I am working on a job not for a wage alone, but I am also performing socially useful deeds." "I am not merely keeping house, but also making a home."

LISTEN TO YOUR HEART

There is nothing in human experience that can give you such a deep feeling of peace and strength as an unshakable belief in a Supreme Being and the act of service to your fellow man. Man has always found a great comfort in the knowledge that powerful forces for good operate within him.

All life gives abundantly. We forget that much genuine goodness is deeply ingrained in all human beings. You can either smother this goodness or encourage it to blossom. Deny your more generous instincts and you become tense and miserable without knowing why. Obey your impulse of generosity, and your heart will fill with gladness.

Don't ask yourself if you can afford to be generous. Ask yourself instead—can you afford *not* to be? Ours is a world of plenty, if we use its resources wisely. The greatest joy the human heart can experience is in working with others for the common good. Spiritually and materially we *profit by being* humane in our attitudes and social conduct. Even the poorest and weakest individual is able to contribute *something* to the welfare of others.

In most situations your conscience usually tells you what is relatively "good" or "evil." While absolute good and utterly detestable evil are readily apparent, our conduct usually expresses itself in varying degrees between these absolute poles. Conscience is a sensitive indicator which keeps us traveling along proper paths. One of the criteria by which it functions is: Will our actions be of benefit to others as well as to ourselves? If the answer is affirmative, then our deeds fall in the realm of goodness.

TESTS FOR SPIRITUAL RELAXATION

How can you tell whether or not you are spiritually relaxed? The skeptic, benevolent or hostile, is entitled to some certainty in this respect. Hence, test yourself:

1. When troubles or losses beset you, do you easily become depressed, and lose faith and hope? Or do you take

your adversities in your stride, rest from the shock, and go on working as before?

2. Do you believe that many a downfall may prepare you for an upward climb to still greater heights than you have formerly reached?

3. Are you aware that good things do not come to us if we do no more than wait? But they can materialize if we aspire, pray, work, and persevere.

4. Do you find spiritual comfort in having done your very best on a given job or occasion, even if that "best" fell short of what seemed to be needed?

5. Do you derive inherent satisfaction from the doing of a good deed? Or do you expect immediate monetary remuneration?

6. Do your moments of spiritual relaxation free you at least temporarily from the turmoil of anxiety, hate, or guilt, so that you can better appraise any situation that may be troubling you?

7. Do you expect nothing but good fortune and pleasures to come your way?

To one who has come this far in considering the problem, the proper answers should be obvious.

In a spiritually relaxed state, your mind is not a blank, neither is it in the so-called "higher celestial spheres." You are not asleep; you are fully aware that you exist; and you are surely not in a trance, but you are totally indifferent to all "outer" disturbances or influences. You also experience a feeling of your true importance.

ONE WAY TO HAPPY LIVING

How can you possess more radiant health and be filled with a greater zest for useful living? Basically, the answer lies in getting close to the stream of life—a common force that expresses itself in every creature throughout all Nature. But to tap that mighty force you must:

1. See that your internal machinery (brain, nerves, glands, organs, etc.) functions without interference. Make sure that your body is properly refreshed and nourished.

2. Become fully aware that you possess some spark of spiritual power within you. Keep that everlasting force harnessed and under control, and direct it into channels of creative effort, joyful living, simple goodness, and community service.

3. Increase your self-understanding. Rule out all self-deception. Check up on your drives, life values, and attitudes, making sure that your energies are utilized for constructive purposes.

4. Find joy in all your work, play, and recreation.

Cultivated intelligence and reason are precious assets but must never blur your *innate* wisdom. How can this innate resource manifest itself frequently to you? Simply by letting yourself become completely and perfectly *calm*. In that state, you know better what to do and what not to do; when to depend upon others and when to depend solely upon yourself. Furthermore, in a state of calmness you may attain greater patience, more understanding, and sharper clarification of all your thoughts.

You thus become aware that you are blessed with a comparatively good life; that you have been given the capacity to choose between "good" and "evil"; that the spark of divinity is operating through you; that you have the responsibility as well as the equipment to carve a definite niche in life for yourself, and that you can be of value to yourself and to your fellow man. That awareness, above all, will give you inner peace.

Bibliography

Allport, Gordon W., *Personality, a Psychological Interpretation*, Henry Holt & Company, Inc., New York, 1937.

Bates, William H., M.D., *Better Eyesight Without Glasses*, Henry Holt & Company, Inc., New York, 1943.

Bettelheim, Bruno, *Love Is Not Enough*, The Free Press, Glencoe, Illinois, 1950.

Bleuler, E., *Textbook on Psychiatry*, The Macmillan Company, New York, 1930.

Boynton, W. H., "Posture as a Condition of Efficient Brain Activity," *School and Society*, Vol. IV, p. 86, 1916.

Brackett, A. C., *Technique of Rest*, Harper & Brothers, New York, 1892.

Brun, Rudolph, M.D., *General Theory of Neuroses*, International University Press, Inc., New York, 1951.

Bull, Nina, *The Attitude Theory of Emotion*, Nervous and Mental Disease Monographs, New York, 1951.

Burnham, W. H., "Posture as a Condition of Efficient Brain Activity," *School and Society*, Vol. IV, No. 86, 1916.

Cabot, Richard C., *What Men Live By*, Houghton Mifflin Company, Boston, 1914.

Call, Annie Payson, *Power Through Repose*, Little, Brown and Company, Boston, 1923.

Cannon, Walter B., *Wisdom of the Body*, W. W. Norton & Company, Inc., New York, 1932.

Cowles, E. S., M.D., *Don't Be Afraid*, Whittlesey House, New York, 1941.

Dercum, F. X., M.D., *Rest and Suggestion*, Blakiston, Philadelphia, 1917.

Deschin, Jacob, *Say It with Your Camera*, McGraw-Hill Book Company, Inc., New York, 1952.

Dorsey, George A., *Hows and Whys of Human Behavior*, Harper & Brothers, New York, 1929.

Federal Security Agency, *The Child*, Vol. XVI, No. 8, April, 1952.

Feldenkrais, M., *Body and Mature Behavior*, International University Press, Inc., New York, 1949.

Fink, D. H., *Release from Nervous Tension*, Simon and Schuster, Inc., New York, 1943.

Fisher, James T., M.C., and Hawley, Lowell S., *A Few Buttons Missing*, J. B. Lippincott Company, Philadelphia, 1951.

Freud, Sigmund, *Basic Writings of Sigmund Freud*, Random House, New York, 1938.

Fried, R. S., "Ten Years of Relaxation and Self-Direction at Bailey Hall," *American Journal of Mental Deficiencies*, 45, 459–463, 1941.

Gates, Arthur I., Jersild, Arthur T., McConnell, T. R., and Challman, Robert C., *Educational Psychology*, The Macmillan Company, New York, 1950.

Gesell, Arnold, M.D., and Ilg, Frances L., M.D., *The Child from Five to Ten*, Harper & Brothers, New York, 1946.

Giddings, G., "Normal Sleep Pattern for Children," *Journal of the American Medical Association*, Vol. 102, pp. 525–529, 1934.

Goldthwait, J. E., *et al.*, *Essentials of Body Mechanics*, J. B. Lippincott Company, Philadelphia, 1945.

Hartmann, George W., *Educational Psychology*, American Book Company, New York, 1941.

Hiltner, C. Ward, *Pastoral Counseling*, Abingdon-Cokesbury Press, Nashville, 1951.

Horney, Karen, *Our Inner Conflicts*, W. W. Norton & Company, Inc., New York, 1945.

——, *Self-Analysis*, W. W. Norton & Company, Inc., New York, 1942.

Hubbard, Elbert, *Notebook of Elbert Hubbard*, Wm. H. Wise & Company, Inc., New York, 1927.

Jacobson, Edmund, M.D., *Progressive Relaxation*, The University of Chicago Press, Chicago, 1929.

Jacobson, Edmund, *You Must Relax*, Whittlesey House, New York, 1934.

James, William, *Habit*, Henry Holt & Company, Inc., New York, 1890.

——, *On Vital Reserves*, Henry Holt & Company, Inc., New York, 1911.

——, *Principles of Psychology*, Vol. II, Henry Holt & Company, Inc., New York, 1902.

——, *Talks to Teachers*, Henry Holt & Company, Inc., New York, 1899.

——, *The Varieties of Religious Experience*, Modern Library, New York, 1902.

Johnson, H. M., Swan, T. H., and Weigand, G. E., "In What Positions Do Healthy People Sleep?" *Journal of the American Medical Association*, Vol. 94, pp. 2058–2068, 1930.

Kearney, Paul W., *How to Drive Better and Avoid Accidents*, Thomas Y. Crowell Company, New York, 1953.

Laird, Donald A., Ph.D., Sc.D., and Muller, Charles G., *Sleep*, John Day Company, Inc., New York, 1930.

Lawton, George, *Aging Successfully*, Columbia University Press, New York, 1947.

Levy, John, and Munroe, Ruth, *The Happy Family*, Alfred A. Knopf, Inc., New York, 1938.

Liebman, Joshua Loth, *Peace of Mind,* Simon and Schuster, Inc., New York, 1946.

—— (editor), *Psychiatry and Religion,* Beacon Press, Boston, 1948.

McKinney, Fred, *Psychology of Personal Adjustment,* John Wiley & Sons, Inc., New York, 1949.

Maslow, A. H., Ph.D., and Mittelman, E., M.D., *Principles of Abnormal Psychology,* Harper & Brothers, New York, 1941.

Menninger, Karl, *Love Against Hate,* Harcourt, Brace and Company, Inc., New York, 1942.

——, *The Human Mind,* Alfred A. Knopf, Inc., New York, 1937.

Morgan, Clifford T., *Physiological Psychology,* McGraw-Hill Book Company, Inc., New York, 1943.

Muncie, Wendell, M.D., *Psychobiology and Psychiatry,* C. V. Mosby Company, St. Louis, 1948.

Overstreet, Bonaro W., *Understanding Fear,* Harper & Brothers, New York, 1951.

Overstreet, H. A., *About Ourselves,* W. W. Norton & Company, Inc., New York, 1927.

——, *The Mature Mind,* W. W. Norton & Company, Inc., New York, 1949.

Pavlov, I. P., *Conditioned Reflexes and Psychiatry,* International Publishers Company, New York, 1941.

Peale, Norman Vincent, D.D., and Blanton, Smiley, M.D., *The Art of Real Happiness,* Prentice-Hall, Inc., New York, 1950.

Pitkin, Walter B., *Road to a Richer Life,* Ziff-Davis Publishing Company, New York, 1949.

——, *Take It Easy,* Simon and Schuster, Inc., New York, 1936.

Poffenberger, A. T., *Principles of Applied Psychology,* Appleton-Century-Crofts, Inc., New York, 1927.

Rathbone, Josephine L., *Relaxation*, Bureau of Publications, Teachers College, Columbia University, 1943.

Reymert, Martin L. (editor), *Feelings and Emotions*, McGraw-Hill Book Company, Inc., New York, 1950.

Richards, T. W., Ph.D., *Modern Clinical Psychology*, McGraw-Hill Book Company, Inc., New York, 1946.

Rogers, Carl, *Counselling and Psychotherapy*, Houghton-Mifflin Company, Boston, 1942.

Roon, K., *New Ways to Relax*, Greystone Press, New York, 1949.

Seabury, David, *Adventures in Self-Discovery*, Whittlesey House, New York, 1938.

————, *Unmasking Our Minds*, Liveright Publishing Corporation, New York, 1924.

Shaffer, Laurance Frederic, Ph.D., *The Psychology of Adjustment*, Houghton Mifflin Company, Boston, 1936.

Snyder, William U., *Casebook of Non-Directive Counseling*, Houghton Mifflin Company, Boston, 1947.

Stagner, Ross, *Psychology of Personality*, McGraw-Hill Book Company, Inc., New York, 1948.

Staples, Frank A., *Water-Color Painting Is Fun*, McGraw-Hill Book Company, New York, 1948.

Strecker, Edward A., M.D., Sc.D., and Appel, Kenneth E., M.D., Sc.D., *Discovering Ourselves*, The Macmillan Company, New York, 1947.

Thorpe, Louis P., Ph.D., and Katz, Barney, Ph.D., *The Psychology of Abnormal Behavior*, The Ronald Press Company, New York, 1948.

U. S. Department of Agriculture, "Posture in Housework," November, 1951.

Vaughan, Wayland F., *Social Psychology*, The Odyssey Press, Inc., New York, 1948.

Walton, Harry, *Plastics for the Home Craftsman,* McGraw-Hill Book Company, Inc., New York, 1951.

Weiss, Edward, M.D., and English, O. Spurgeon, M.D., *Psychosomatic Medicine,* W. B. Saunders Company, Philadelphia, 1943.

Woodworth, Robert S., and Marquis, Donald G., *Psychology,* Henry Holt & Company, Inc., New York, 1947.

Yates, D. H., "Relaxation in Psychotherapy," *Journal of General Psychology,* Vol. 34, pp. 213–237, 1946.

Index